SO YOU WANT TO BE A
PHYSICIAN ASSISTANT

YOUR GUIDE TO A NEW CAREER

D1313830

Beth Grivett, PA-C

So You Want to Be a Physician Assistant

Your Guide to a New Career

Beth Grivett, PA-C
http://www.physicianassistantbooks.com
beth@physicianassistantbooks.com

Lightning Source
www.lightningsource.com
1246 Heil Quaker Blvd.
La Vergne, TN USA 37086
inquiry@lightningsource.com

Book Design by Denise Werner

First Printing May 2009
ISBN-10: 0-615-28354-3
ISBN-13: 978-0-615-28354-8

Printed in the United States of America

Dedicated to future physician assistants
and to those who have helped to shape this extraordinary profession.

Contents

Appendices

Acknowledgements

Thank you to all who helped me to put this book together. It is truly a collection of great minds in the profession and would not be nearly as enlightening without the input of the following:

Nancy Langdon Jones, CFP® whose book *So You Want to Be a Financial Planner* was my inspiration and guide. It took me a few years to get the guts to dive into the world of writing and self-publishing, but without your hand-holding I would be lost. You are not only a great mom, but also an example of a strong, professional woman whom I aspire to emulate.

Gaye Breyman, my dear friend and colleague. Our nearly daily conversations about the direction of the profession, PA politics, and volunteers have become such a treasured part of my life. You are a creative and ambitious woman who has helped to me to gain confidence to become an effective PA leader and take on projects beyond my abilities!

Larry Rosen, PA-C, who is forever keeping me in line and facing me in the right direction while living the example of the epitome of the profession. Thank for you everything you do to promote the positive aspects of being a PA to the general public and to our potential employers, the physicians. Your insight is brilliant.

Brian and Cynthia who make up my wonderful little family and who put up with my travel for PA leadership and weekends filled with writing newsletter articles and board reports. Your support is unwavering. Thank you for loving me for who I am.

All the contributors to this book – you willingly allowed me to publish a perfect picture of your PA world without question and I thank you for your time and your commitment to the growth of this career.

Dan, thank you for your awesome editing talents!

All the staff and volunteer leadership at the **American Academy of Physician Assistants** and its constituent organizations. Your hours of dedication to the profession are often under recognized but absolutely invaluable. And especially to the staff and volunteer leadership at the **California Academy of Physician Assistants** whom I rely upon daily and with whom I look forward to working, year after year.

And a big thank you to my team at **Newport Family Medicine.** You have shaped me professionally and educated me about medicine. You willingly put up with my frantic lifestyle, crazy ideas and overcommitted schedule. From the partners and associates to the staff, you all have become such great friends and colleagues. I cannot imagine a better fit for me as a PA.

Foreword

Good move. You bought Beth's book (or borrowed a friend's copy). Either way, I suspect you're reading this because you've been thinking long and hard about becoming a PA. Thousands of questions and as many doubts have crossed your mind. Keep reading. You're about to see your troubled landscape much more clearly.

In *So You Want To Be a Physician Assistant,* Beth Grivett has skillfully articulated just about every reason to become a PA…and about every reason not to. Hers is a spot-on, thoughtful, honestly-stripped-of-the-window-dressing look at one of this country's most sought after and fastest growing professions.

It's true; thousands apply and few are chosen. But be comforted. You now have a leg up. As you navigate the chapters that follow, you will find safe footing and enlightenment, the product of Beth's fourteen years not only as an exceptional family practice clinician but as a profession leader, prized and respected by her colleagues everywhere. Her first person narrative escorts you through the schooling, the job search, the specialties, the physician guided team model, and the mine fields of juggling life, love and work and coming out whole on the other end.

As I read Beth's book, I couldn't help thinking of the legendary Arthur Godfrey (or is everyone too young to remember him on radio?) In his broadcasts, Godfrey had the singular ability to make you feel like he was talking only to you. Beth's writing style, laced with humor, is easy and personal; as if she were sitting in your living room helping you puzzle together all the pieces of information you'll need to make a sound decision.

Among the gifts of my life, I count my friendship with Beth. She is both sunshine and safeguard to a man who more than occasionally leads with his feelings and requires a compassionate but firm course correction to reality. Beth calls me her "mentor" but, in truth, it is clearly so much the other way around; reading her book only confirms the sweep of her wisdom and intuition, sources of comfort I plan to draw from for as long as she'll allow.

So You Want To Be a Physician Assistant? The decision is daunting. Make no mistake, it is one challenging prize; demanding and competitive but worth every torturous obstacle each of us has had to overcome to win it.

I wish you well in your deliberations. Your author, intent on honoring the promise each reader brings to the process, says it best:

"Once you are accepted in a program, you will work hard but you have made it there because you are supposed to be there."

Spot on, Ms. Grivett

Larry Rosen, PA-C

Why?

I met a PA for the first time because of the advice from a physician. I worked at Childrens Hospital Los Angeles while an undergraduate at UCLA. I knew I needed to get some hands-on experience to enhance my medical school application. But, in reality, it was a better job than working on campus because I could pull all the weekend and holiday shifts which paid overtime to help meet tuition and rent. My job title was "Physical Therapy Aide" and included everything from transferring kids in and out of their wheelchairs, to splinting and casting, to burn and wound care in the hydrotherapy room. What an amazing experience to work so closely with the physical and occupational therapists, speech therapists, social workers, child life specialists and nurses. They practiced a true team approach to medicine and respected and admired one another's contributions to the child's progress in the Rehabilitation Unit.

Supriya worked primarily in rheumatology, mostly seeing kids diagnosed with juvenile rheumatoid arthritis. I admired her skills but didn't have a strong desire to go into physical therapy. I really looked up to her husband, Neal, who had achieved what I couldn't even imagine yet – a residency position in the Pediatric Intensive Care Unit. I didn't even know if I could ever get into medical school. I was doing well as a kinesiology major and was really enjoying the upper division classes once organic chemistry was finally over! But, it seemed so distant. Here I almost had my degree and was overwhelmed with working enough to pay the bills while my classmates were taking the whole quarter off from school to study for the MCATs! One day Neal took me aside and told me that I should meet a PA with whom he had worked. He told me that he thought I was much more of a physician assistant type than a physician type. Whatever!?! I didn't know at the time what a complement that was – maybe he didn't mean it to be, but he clearly saw me for what I was. Although Neal and Supriya are clear across the country in Nashville, we still keep in touch and he tries to get away from the ICU long enough to vacation with us every now and then!

Most PAs who you meet will have a story like mine. Those of us in practice more than 10 years or so had never heard of a PA growing up, and possibly even through our first career. We didn't graduate from high school and think, "I want to be a PA when I grow up." Why? Because we had never met one. Moreover, there weren't very many! The PA profession is young. I know this for a fact because the first class graduated the year I was born – and I am not old. Back when corpsmen were coming home from Vietnam, these men with vast medical experience, who had been treating injuries of war, couldn't work as civilians because they didn't have a medical or nursing degree. The brilliant Eugene Stead, MD saw an opportunity amidst the projection of a physician shortage. In a 1964 letter explaining his concept of the profession, Dr. Stead wrote, "These men will be trained as physician assistants. Their purpose will be to extend the arms and brains of the physician so that he can care for more people." Shortly thereafter he created the first Physician Assistant Program at Duke University and the first class of THREE graduated in 1967 - Victor H. Germino, Kenneth F. Ferrell and Richard J. Scheele.[1] There continued to be military applicants and graduates, but others with various types of medical experience applied to the programs and saw the potential to do more as a PA. Back then jobs were scarce. Many states had PA programs, but graduating students were working without official recognition of the profession or licensure. It took years to change state laws and start licensing PAs. And even though many PAs enjoyed an amicable practice setting due to the work of our "father" PAs, we only just in the year 2000 celebrated having Mississippi become the last state to finally enact legislation allowing PAs to obtain licensure and practice legally!

So, you didn't get into medical school? Yeah, some of us always thought we would be a doctor. I know I did. Ask my mom – I had a toy microscope in 2nd grade and was dissecting bugs for fun after school in Jr. High! I knew I wanted to go into medicine, and I wanted to be the decision maker. Since all I knew was "doctor" that is where I was headed. Patients unclear about the concept still ask me when I will be done with medical school! I tell them this is my career and I love it. Then they will say – but, you are just

---

1   http://www.pahx.org

as good as a physician, so why aren't you one? That is when I say, "Thank you" (because I feel complemented), "but why would I be a physician if I am good at what I am doing right now?" Am I a failure because I didn't go to medical school? Quite the opposite! I won't ever make the same amount of money as a physician can, but I found a career that allowed me to attend an abbreviated medical school – with less investment of time and money. I started seeing patients right out of school because I learned my limitations and to know what I didn't know. I work hard and sometimes long hours, but I do not have the responsibility of running a practice. I have paperwork and meetings to go to, but that is a small portion of my role which is primarily direct patient care.

The promise of a growing career

I was at a diabetes conference held by Johnson & Johnson in the fall of 2008. Kim Kelly, PharmD[2], who is the Director of the Diabetes Program, told us about the audience for the conference. There were no physicians invited. There were only diabetes educators, nurse practitioners and physician assistants. Yeah, we were sort of curious since we are used to going to conferences and learning alongside physicians. He said that J&J had done a lot of research in diabetes and how to provide the best care to this quickly growing patient population. Then he quoted the Hall-of-Fame hockey player Wayne Gretzky in saying "I skate to where the puck is *going to be*, not where it has been."[3] When referring to the audience they had invited to this program, he was explaining what they knew from their research. There are less and less physicians going into primary care. In our aging society with such an enormous number of patients living long past retirement age, we as a society are going to be lacking sufficient numbers of healthcare providers and especially primary care providers. J&J wisely envisioned an amazing weekend-long education program about diabetes not to educate physicians, but to educate the non-physician providers which we are all going to be relying extensively on in the future.

---

2   http://www.jjdi.us/faculty/index.html

3   http://www.brainyquote.com

What I didn't know when I applied to PA school is how accepted PAs would become. Although it sounded like a good career 15-20 years ago, now it has become a *great* career. In fact US News and World Report continues to rate the physician assistant as a top career – again in the top 30 careers for 2009.[4]

> *U.S. News has plowed through hundreds of careers, looking for the jobs with the best outlook in this recessionary economy (and beyond), the highest rates of job satisfaction, the least difficult training necessary, the most prestige, and the highest pay. These careers have staying power: They're smart moves now, and they'll be smart moves for years to come.*

> *The aging of the baby boomer generation promises to place major demands on the healthcare system. There will be more need for physical therapists as active seniors work their way back from hip and knee replacements. A couple of national surveys also found that physical therapists rank high in job satisfaction. Registered nurses, biomedical equipment technicians, and physician assistants will also be in hot demand. Equipment technicians install, train, calibrate, and maintain a cadre of fast-evolving medical equipment, such as PET/CT scanners and robotic radiosurgery units. Computer systems know-how is increasingly useful, and you can be an everyday hospital hero after only a two-year associate's degree. Physician assistants need two or three years of postgraduate education. Then they can do about 80 percent of what physicians do, and their salaries can reach six figures.*

I have a long time dear friend, Dr. Jay Cohen, who has been supportive of the PA profession since before I had the pleasure of working for him as a PA in his family practice. He has been engaged in health care delivery for nearly three decades, and is keenly aware of the challenges and opportunities which currently exist within the medical industry. Like

---

4   http://www.usnews.com/articles/business/best-careers/2008/12/11/the-30-best-careers-for -2009.html

most other health care professionals, Dr. Cohen entered the field because of his desire to improve the lives of others. What he soon realized was that his clinical expertise as a board certified emergency physician alone would not be enough to achieve his desired goals. So midway through his career, he returned to school to become certified as a physician executive as well. He has learned that the role of the physician assistant is an integral part of an effective health care delivery system.

Clinically, Dr. Cohen served the first half of his professional career as an emergency physician and the second half as a primary care physician in private practice. In both capacities he worked with PAs. As a physician executive, he co-founded a very large and hugely successful Southern California Independent Practice Association (IPA). He is also now serving as the board chair of one of the largest associations of accountable physician groups dedicated to improving patients' health using the principles of coordinated care. Dr. Cohen shares his views regarding the important role PAs play, first based on his perceptions as a clinician and then as a health care executive.

> *From my experience in the patient-care setting, physicians find themselves accountable for large numbers of complex patient problems, for which they too often either don't have the time or expertise to address on their own. For these reasons, the most effective clinical practices are collaborative efforts that include various health care professionals (i.e. physicians, pharmacists, social workers, therapists, nurses, and PAs). In both my emergency medical practice and subsequent primary care practice, PAs proved to be invaluable contributors as members of the professional teams.*
>
> *In the Emergency Department setting, PAs represent a cost-effective way to relieve patient over-crowding and prolonged wait times during peak hours. They also assist with more efficient triage and disposition of patients by freeing the more highly-trained emergency physician to focus her time and attention on the select patients more acutely in need of her specific expertise.*

Similarly, PAs were an essential element of the efficient operation of my primary care practice. Properly trained and supervised, they truly serve as "extenders" of physicians' capabilities, allowing the health care needs of a greater number of patients to be fulfilled by fewer physicians. This vital role will continue to increase in importance as our physician shortage rapidly progresses to its full extent.

From the perspective of an executive in the managed care industry, the aforementioned principles apply to an even greater extent. As we strive to improve the health, well-being, and daily lives of large populations of patients, the efficiency and effectiveness of the delivery system becomes even more important.

On a widespread basis, accountable physician groups have designed and implemented systems that improve patients' access to care, the quality of their clinical outcomes, and the relative costs incurred. This has been achieved by the efficient use of available resources that enable the delivery of the right care by the right professional at the right place and the right time. PAs are routinely making important contributions as participants on these integrated delivery system teams. Interdisciplinary clinical teams such as these will become increasingly more common and serve as the Advanced Medical Home to more efficiently meet the complex needs of the patient populations we serve.

As our nation searches for solutions to the challenges associated with rising health care costs, increasing numbers of uninsured, physician shortages, and widespread variance in our health care delivery systems and the outcomes they produce, it is clear that collaborative efforts will be required to meet the needs of our patients. PAs, working with physicians, and other health care professionals who have embraced the principles of coordinated care, will serve as an increasingly essential element of the solutions to the challenges we face.

And it isn't only a physician's perception that PAs are the future. The number crunchers have us figured out as well. The US Bureau of Labor

Statistics Occupational Outlook, 2008-09 Edition, indicates strong growth for the profession.[5]

> *Employment of physician assistants is expected to grow 27 percent from 2006 to 2016, much faster than the average for all occupations. Projected rapid job growth reflects the expansion of health care industries and an emphasis on cost containment, which results in increasing use of PAs by health care establishments.*

> *Physicians and institutions are expected to employ more PAs to provide primary care and to assist with medical and surgical procedures because PAs are cost-effective and productive members of the health care team. Physician assistants can relieve physicians of routine duties and procedures. Telemedicine— using technology to facilitate interactive consultations between physicians and physician assistants—also will expand the use of physician assistants.*

> *Besides working in traditional office-based settings, PAs should find a growing number of jobs in institutional settings such as hospitals, academic medical centers, public clinics, and prisons. PAs also may be needed to augment medical staffing in inpatient teaching hospital settings as the number of hours physician residents are permitted to work is reduced, encouraging hospitals to use PAs to supply some physician resident services.*

> *Job opportunities for PAs should be good, particularly in rural and inner-city clinics because those settings have difficulty attracting physicians. In addition to job openings from employment growth, openings will result from the need to replace physician assistants who retire or leave the occupation permanently during the 2006-16 decade. Opportunities will be best in states that allow PAs a wider scope of practice, such as allowing PAs to prescribe medications.*

---

5   http://www.bls.gov/oco/ocos081.htm

Is this career right for everyone? Absolutely not! Becoming a PA is **not** a stepping stone to medical school. If you want to be a doctor – go to medical school. If you are uncomfortable as a dependent practitioner, this is the wrong place to be. You won't be happy with yourself and you won't be fair to your patients if you cannot work as a member of the team. As a PA, you must constantly remember that you are there in place of the physician and he is counting on you to make the decisions he would make were he sitting in front of that patient. On the other hand, this is not an easy path to a job where you can "act" like a doctor. You have got to know your stuff. And, like a physician, you can never stop learning. Research is ongoing in every field of medicine and you have to keep up on new guidelines and new advances in technology. You also have to nurture the relationships with people who will help you find the information you don't know!

What is the difference between a Physician Assistant and a Nurse Practitioner?

I am getting this question out of the way early. I know the answer well because I am asked at least once a month by a patient and from time to time by other healthcare professionals. I have attempted to explain it to legislators in numerous settings. In fact, I got so good at explaining the difference in a "politically correct" way that during presentations about the physician-physician assistant team given to physicians for the California Academy of Physician Assistants (CAPA)[6], I was chosen from our panel as the designated PA to answer that question – and it was asked every time we gave the presentation. Sometimes my answer changes a little depending on the audience, but the bottom line answer is mostly "not much." If a patient called an office, like the one where I work, with both a PA and NP there, either could see that patient. And, ultimately, the patient will be examined and treated appropriately and will likely be quite satisfied with the care they received. Both the PA and NP can order any necessary testing, write prescriptions, do referrals and provide the patient with any educational information they need. But in reality, if you look deep enough, there are subtle differences in the way we practice.

---

6   http://www.capanet.org

The independent practice issue is where we definitely part ways. PAs are <u>dependent</u> practitioners and, as a rule, strive to predict how their supervising physician would treat the patient before him if he was in the room. We learn that from the beginning of PA school. We are members of the team that treat the patients in the practice, but the leader of the team is always the physician. Only after working with a physician or group for a few years does the PA learn all the preferences and the styles of the practice to make the patients feel confident that although the physician is not physically present in the room, the care given is based in large part upon knowledge the PA has gained by working on that health care team. Independent vs. Dependent is really the bottom line – NPs consider themselves to be independent practitioners while PAs consider themselves to be dependent (upon the physician). One approach is not better than the other necessarily, but PAs reinforce team practice in their daily visits with patients and avoid taking "ownership" of a patient throughout the disease course. It is no secret that there are NPs that practice completely independently and that is legal in many states. They have agreements with local physicians for consult, but can run their own offices and see patients independently.

The American Academy of Nurse Practitioners (AANP)[7] has a position paper on NP practice that states the following:

> *The autonomous nature of the nurse practitioner's advanced clinical practice requires accountability for health care outcomes. Insuring the highest quality of care requires certification, periodic peer review, clinical outcome evaluations, a code for ethical practice, evidence of continuing professional development and maintenance of clinical skills. Nurse Practitioners are committed to seeking and sharing knowledge that promotes quality health care and improves clinical outcomes. This is accomplished by leading and participating in both professional and lay health care forums, conducting research, and applying findings to clinical practice.*

---

7   http://www.aanp.org

Nothing in the statement considers physician involvement or oversight because of the independent provider focus of that profession. In fact, NPs reference "peer review" which many consider to be review of their daily practice by other NPs rather than by physicians.

Compare that with the statement from The American Academy of Physician Assistants (AAPA)[8]:

> *Physician assistants are health care professionals licensed, or in the case of those employed by the federal government they are credentialed, to practice medicine with physician supervision. As part of their comprehensive responsibilities, PAs conduct physical exams, diagnose and treat illnesses, order and interpret tests, counsel on preventive health care, assist in surgery, and write prescriptions. Within the physician-PA relationship, physician assistants exercise autonomy in medical decision making and provide a broad range of diagnostic and therapeutic services. A PA's practice may also include education, research, and administrative services. Because of the close working relationship the PAs have with physicians, PAs are educated in the medical model designed to complement physician training.*

PAs are not completely autonomous or independent, but can make relevant clinical decisions without consulting with a physician. We are certainly accountable for our medical decision making for our patients, but we are equally accountable to our supervising physician(s) for providing the type of care that they expect for their patients. Even after a PA has decades of experience under his belt and has provided services to tens of thousands of patients, and even when a PA is involved in training medical students and PA students, that PA is still a dependent practitioner working as part of a physician-led team. Marie Gilbert, PA-C works in otolarygology and beautifully describes her relationship with her supervising physician the way many of us would if we were so eloquent!

> *I'd say my 22-year working relationship with my supervising physician (and a 6-year relationship with our second physician)*

---

8   http://www.aapa.org

is one of sincere mutual respect and trust. The physicians are always available to me by phone or in the clinic for guidance as needed. They review some of my charts regularly as a part of our compliance program and we discuss difficult or unusual cases on a daily basis, as they present. My degree of independence has increased over the years to coincide with my increased abilities, so I don't believe independent practice laws are needed in my specialty or for PAs in general.

The physicians are also supportive of my efforts with teaching PA students and my work for AAPA and the Society of PAs in Otolaryngology. They come to me for my opinions on clinical and administrative issues. I would say I am allowed to be as independent as I want and am trusted to ask for help when I need it; truly we are a team in that respect.

What about education? Well, there are different paths to becoming a nurse practitioner and a physician assistant. The PA generally has some medical experience and college education before applying to PA school. The PA program is a medical program for further training to work alongside a physician as a dependent practitioner in a team model. The training is a combination of classroom and clinical training (I expand a lot on this in Chapter 2). The clinical training consists of rotations in specialty inpatient settings as well as outpatient office settings. An NP is a registered nurse initially, who generally has many years of experience working as a nurse, and then goes back to school for an advanced nursing degree. The majority of NP clinical training is done in the outpatient office setting.

Are there turf issues? There are some - more so in some settings than others. Most of the "battles" are legislative and deal with specifics of the practice act in the state. For the most part NPs and PAs work together well, but may compete for the same jobs. Which is better? The PA, of course! But, I am biased. What I have sensed, however, is that the physician organizations I have worked with on legislative issues tend to feel a little less threatened by the PA profession in some situations. We cannot exist without our physician partners. We do not want to expand our scope of practice above and beyond that which the supervising physician is comfortable. We love learning from our physicians and we love being on our physician-led teams. By not attempting to gain more independence, we keep a good relationship with physicians. We can usually count on our physician organizations and medical boards to understand, and often even support us, because our ultimate goal is to make the life of the physician a little easier by lessening their workload.

What's in a Name?

Many organizations attempt to lump PAs and NPs into one category. It makes sense when there are NPs and PAs in the same office performing the same services. Sometimes nurse midwives are also included in our group of "someone who is not a physician but providing medical services." We are often all treated the same as far as benefits and salary, as well as many duties and responsibilities. You'll hear a lot of weird attempts at giving us an all-inclusive type of a name. Some you will like and some you will feel are barely palatable, but they are out there in studies and in institutions, so you will have to just get used to it. You will hear:

Non-Physician Provider

Midlevel Provider

Physician Extender

What does it all mean? It means people don't have time and don't want to spell out Nurse Practitioner and/or Physician Assistant. Maybe writing all that will make them exceed their texting allowance! Regardless, when they say these things, they are generally referring to the group of NPs and PAs and maybe also nurse midwives.

How about changing the name of our profession? Seasoned PAs out there reading this are thinking, "Oh no, Beth, are you really going to go there?" We listen to this argument every few years at the American Academy of Physician Assistants (AAPA) House of Delegates meeting. Most states have their laws written to allow "Physician Assistants" to practice medicine. Some call us Physician*'s* Assistants. There are many PAs and PA students who want a new name. For whatever reason, they feel the word *Assistant* is demeaning. I have to say, in all my years of being a student and in practice, I haven't had a patient tell me or my supervising physician that she didn't think she could trust me because I was just an "assistant." They may ask about the profession if they are unfamiliar, but they don't advise me to attempt to change our name. My friend and mentor, Larry, has been a PA a little longer than me – he jokingly says he thinks we should just be called "Klemdon." I don't really know what that means, but it would probably make life a lot easier on us. Then we wouldn't be re-working words that exist in the English language and trying to find the exact fit that doesn't exist.

The more common suggestion that comes up frequently is *Physician Associate*. Somehow being an associate feels a little more comfortable to people than being an assistant. And, we could still be "PAs" if we were physician associates. Seems harmless, right? Well, no. First, consider the expense. Just in my own practice I would have to create new business cards, order a new sign for the door, and get a new lab coat. Now consider the expense a large organization like the New York State Society of Physician Assistants would incur changing letterhead and websites, the education materials, etc. All the PA programs would have to look into changing the degree or certificate they awarded to a physician associate. Ok, so it is expensive. Worse yet, though, are the laws that govern the profession. Basically, every state would need to go through every regulation and state law and change the word *Assistant* to the word *Associate* in order to legally practice. Talk about expensive <u>and scary</u>. If your entire practice act is up for review and must be voted on, then maybe a legislator would want to put more restrictions on what you can do, or get rid of the licensing of that profession altogether. So, you might look back and wonder how they settled on *Physician Assistant* and you might think it is not the most appropriate name, but we are stuck with it, so embrace it!

Now you know a little more about what a PA is, where the profession came from and where it might be going. You know the difference between a physician and a PA and you know the difference between an NP and a PA. If you are OK with all of this and you can deal with being a *Physician Assistant* and not a *Physician Associate*, then it is time to move on to the next chapter and see if you are ready to apply to a PA program!

Back to School

No longer is the PA class filled with seasoned medical professionals who want to change careers. Just a decade ago, a typical class consisted mostly of medical professionals going back to school for a second career. Many classes had a couple of registered nurses, a respiratory technician, an x-ray technician, a paramedic, a surgical tech and maybe even a physician from a foreign country. Usually there was about a hundred years of medical experience and more than few heads of grey hair sitting in the room at orientation. These students are still there, but now you will find that students know that this is the career for them at a younger age. High school and college students have already put in volunteer hours at the local hospital and know what classes they need to meet all the qualifications for admission to a PA program.. We are seeing the average age slowly and consistently decrease over the years. This should not discourage the mature applicant. Do not feel that you will not be accepted because of your age. Most programs are seeking students with real medical experience as their ideal candidate. PA programs pride themselves in not focusing solely on GPA and test scores. They are looking for experienced, well-rounded students that will make great PAs. They are looking to preserve our profession's history to an extent – giving good people enough knowledge to make a difference as a PA.

How do you choose the right program?

First and foremost, make sure the program is accredited by the ARC-PA, the Accreditation Review Commission on Education of the Physician Assistant. The program must be accredited as you graduate in order for you to be eligible to sit for the national board exam and to practice in any state in the US. With all the internet scams out there, be aware! If a program claims that you can "fast-track" or skip steps, be cautious. And, programs can lose their accreditation, too so be sure to check the status at arc-pa.org/Acc_Programs /acc_programs.html.

Talk with a few recently graduated PAs and get a feel for the different programs. Most are primary care programs with a few that emphasize surgery. Committing to a primary care program does not obligate you to work in family practice for the rest of your life. In fact, that is one of the beautiful things about being a PA. You are not obligated to work in any field for the rest of your life, because your training gives you the fundamentals. Your job and your supervising physician will dictate your scope of practice, meaning that as a PA you can only practice the type of medicine that is practiced by your supervising physician. Many PAs do not know in what field they will practice until after graduation from the PA program.

Getting the prerequisites done for school can vary from program to program. I usually tell people that the prerequisites are similar to medical school – you don't have to have an undergraduate degree to get into some PA programs, but you do need the specified number of credits in chemistry, physics, biology, etc. It is worth paying the $35 through the Physician Assistant Education Association (PAEA), at www.paeaonline.org, to get the one-year subscription to the on-line directory of schools if you are undecided about your choices and/or if you want to apply to multiple programs. This gives you access to detailed and updated information about all of the accredited PA programs including curriculum, tuition, degree awarded, and entrance requirements. This website also links to CASPA[1], the Central Application Service for Physician Assistants, where you can submit a centralized application to multiple schools. Note that *not* all schools use the CASPA service, so you will need to apply separately to those programs, but you are required to use the service if the program is enrolled. As of this publication, there are 143 programs in the US with 113 using CASPA for 2009-10, but those numbers are expected to increase a bit.

Location, location, location
You will need a program that meets your needs as far as location and housing is concerned. You have to go to campus. There are no on-line or distance learning programs. Talk with the program about the structure. Some programs require the majority of your time be spent on or near campus while some require less time on campus and more time at clinical

---

1   https://portal.caspaonline.org

sites that you help to line up. If you have relationships with physicians that you want to train with already, make sure the clinical coordinator at your program is aware of that so they can attempt to fit that into your schedule as a training site. But, most programs do not require that you help to line up the clinical sites – they do that for you. Many times your schedule is very different for the first year and second year of the program. Programs may or may not have housing available for students, but they may be able to help you with options. Some students prefer to go to a program in the area where they desire to practice so that they can start networking for a job during rotations, but this is not essential.

What type of credential does the program offer?
This is a big and important question. Now that you understand the origins of the profession, you will surely understand the reason for the big degree debate. As you research different schools, you will find that some give no "degree." You finish the program with a certificate of completion which allows you to sit for the national PA boards and get licensed or registered in most states. There are also programs that award a baccalaureate degree and an increasing number awarding only a master's degree. There is much talk of the new doctorate program soon becoming the standard. Which is the right path? Do you need to have a master's degree? Are those programs better? The answer to both of those questions was probably "no" 10 years ago, but this may be changing. Like many professions that are maturing, especially in healthcare, the push is toward an advanced degree. Physical therapists and pharmacists are getting doctorates now. So, what is the debate? Most would agree that a higher degree gives the profession more credibility and elevates our status among our peers and other members of the healthcare team, and maybe even demands a higher salary. But, what do we give up? Programs that award a certificate or baccalaureate indicate that they generally have a higher minority population and greater diversity within the class. It is hard to know if this is really true. But, because the cost of these programs is generally lower, they may be accepting some students that may never be able to afford a higher degree program. This may imply that they are also more likely to practice in underserved areas where PAs are needed most.

I have spent many years at AAPA House of Delegates meetings across the country listening to this debate year after year and I can tell you, after hours of debate, we end in a draw every year! So, decide what is right for you. I never got my master's degree even though the program I went to now awards one. It probably won't matter in my career because now I have over 10 years of experience and employers tend to like that. I have never been asked during a job interview why I don't have a master's degree, but I truly think that a lot of physicians don't have a clear understanding of how diverse the programs are. Or, maybe they don't care because they knew I finished the program and passed the boards. Will this attitude change in the future? Employers certainly have the right to require a degree of their employees regardless of national certification status, and some do already. It is impossible to predict what hospitals and individual physicians will require of PAs in the future. There is speculation that insurers may start requiring certain levels of education or specific degrees for reimbursement for services provided by PAs, since we have seen this for other health professionals.

Virginia Joslin, PA-C, MPH is Assistant Professor, Division Chief, Emory University Physician Assistant Program, PA Faculty Liaison to the MPH/PA Program and Coordinator of Development, Department of Family and Preventive Medicine. Ms. Joslin was the Director of the Emory PA Program from 1991- 2007 and served as chair of the PAEA Graduate Education Commission, a committee charged with researching the issue of how to define graduate-level education. She is currently a regular site visitor for the ARC-PA for both entry level and post-graduate specialty PA programs. She has been intimately involved in the discussions regarding the "right" degree for our profession and summarizes the pros and cons succinctly in the following:

Physician Assistant Education: How important is the degree?

Of the 142 currently accredited entry-level Physician Assistant Education Programs, 83% award a master's degree, while the remaining 17% of Programs award an undergraduate degree or certificate.[2] The titles of the PA program master degrees also vary: Master in Physician Assistant Studies, Master of Science or Master of Medical Science. Additionally, among PA programs there is a wide range of applicant requirements such as course prerequisites, minimum GPA and standardized exam scores, and health care experience, as well as academic settings, length of training, class size, student/faculty ratio, and cost of tuition plus incidental costs.

Most entry-level PA programs consider the degree they offer to be a professional degree, which is one that reflects a curriculum that prepares the student for the practice of the PA profession, whether the degree awarded is a bachelor or master degree. Since the beginning of the PA profession, the physician assistant curricula has been competency-based and designed after the medical model. The various PA curricula reflect the medical knowledge, skills, and professional behavior expected of a graduate PA. The PA competency-based curriculum and student level of performance is evaluated according to the PA competencies[3], which are comparable to the competencies for medical student graduates and physicians. For PA programs to be accredited by the Accreditation Review Commission on the Education of Physician Assistants, specific minimum standards must be met to provide an adequate educational environment to obtain the professional knowledge and skills necessary for practice.

The trend in many health professions' education, including PA education has been to offer graduate degrees. As the professions of nursing, physical therapy, occupational therapy and others transformed to graduate degree-awarding programs, the Physician Assistant Education Association, formerly named the Association of Physician Assistant Programs, charged several committees to

---

2   24th Annual Report on Physician Assistant Educational Programs (preliminary) Savannah, Oct 2008 (annual report available at: http://www.paeaonline.org/index. php?ht=d/sp/i/208/pid/208)

3   Competencies for the Physician Assistant Profession (available in the appendix and at: http://www.nccpa.net/PAC/Competencies_home.aspx)

research the issue of the appropriate entry-level degree for the PA profession. When the nursing profession decided to offer a clinical doctorate degree, many health professionals including physicians agreed it was to time to study the need for and issues related to clinical doctorate degrees for health professionals other than physicians.

In the spring of 2009, participants including physicians, physician assistants and PA educators in the PA Clinical Doctorate Summit provided a set of recommendations to the national PA professional organizations on the PA degree issue that included: the master's degree is the single entry-level and terminal degree for the profession; the PA profession opposes an entry-level clinical doctorate that is PA specific; the profession supports advanced professional education, including academic post-graduate doctorates that are not specific to the PA profession (examples: Ed.D, Ph.D); and to join the physician education groups in investigating the option for a bridge medical education program for PAs, who are interested in becoming physicians.[4]

When considering application to PA Programs, there are some important factors to be considered as you plan your path to a PA career. The degree awarded is one of these factors. Some states now require a master's degree in PA education to obtain a state license to practice. Some institutions and employers require a master's degree for employment or offer a higher salary to graduate PAs with a master's degree. At this point in time in the majority of states, a graduate PA awarded an undergraduate degree or certificate, particularly one with significant clinical experience, is competitive in the job market. An entry-level master's degree in the PA profession may provide more future advanced career options, or employment options that include participation in clinical research, administration, or leadership roles.

---

4   Informing the Clinical Doctorate Dialogue (available at: http://www.paeaonline.org/index.php?ht=d/sp/i/66891/pid/66891

In national discussions about healthcare reform and workforce diversity, there are concerns expressed about disparities in health and healthcare, and an increasing need for primary care health professionals. In general the cost of PA education is higher at private versus public institutions, and at master's degree-granting PA programs. Most master's degree level PA programs require an applicant to have an undergraduate degree, which means that the applicant will have assumed a debt of at least four years of undergraduate education, and will accumulate an additional debt for their graduate PA degree. A PA program applicant with minimal financial means might be less likely to apply to a master's level PA program. Those PA graduates with a high debt load are more likely to choose practices in a medical or surgical specialty, or in a suburban/urban setting, which offer higher salaries than a primary care or rural setting. Yet the need is the greatest for primary care, some medical specialties, and general surgery providers in inner-city and rural settings that care for medically underserved populations, who experience the higher levels of health disparities.

Advanced degrees do not necessarily reflect added value. The decision to apply to a specific PA program should be a personal value-driven choice. Developing a list of program characteristics that an applicant highly values will help make the decision easier. The most important factors related to the specific PA program should include accreditation status, satisfaction of graduates and their employers, satisfaction and retention rate of current students, faculty and staff, and a high pass rate on the national PA certification exam. Other more personal values to consider are financial resources; program location near home, family or a spouse's job; future practice plans and other career options. If an applicant has an interest in becoming a PA educator or participating in clinical research, an entry-level PA program awarding a master's degree might be a better choice. On the other hand, there are also graduate programs in related fields, such as public health or health administration, including some that are primarily web-based and can be completed while maintaining current employment as a PA. This pathway would provide the flexibility to work in positions in PA education, health administration or research.

A thorough analysis of the depth and content of a PA program's curriculum should guide an applicant in deciding the level of education provided, despite the degree awarded. Unlike applying to colleges, deciding which PA program is the right choice for you should be based on considerable research into the details of specific PA programs weighing the pros and cons of the degree awarded as well as an honest evaluation of an applicant's personal values.

I haven't answered the question about which program is right for you, but I don't know you. Make sure you do your research and consider the discussion. If you already possess a bachelor's degree or are working on one now, the natural progression would be to apply to a program that will award a master's degree. But, I wouldn't discount other programs if they better meet your needs.

What to expect in PA school

I wish someone had told me what to really expect. That's my fault - I should have asked! I know now - **it is intense**. Don't let anyone try to tell you otherwise. Do not accept a seat in a PA program unless you are dedicated and fully committed to completing the program and becoming a PA. You will absolutely need to COMMIT yourself to the program for the duration. Do not plan on being able to work on the side in your current occupation – you will not have time. If you have a family, expect to neglect them. Plan for the inevitable long days of class and long nights of studying followed by crazy hours during clinical rotations. You will be giving up many social and family events to complete the program successfully and to pass the boards. I was always a good student throughout high school. But, I had time to play. I "hung out" after school when I should have been studying, but I continued to bring home good grades. Every now and then I had to cram for a test or spend a whole weekend finishing a project I should have been working on all quarter. I remember getting to UCLA as an undergraduate and being shocked at the level of intensity. All of the sudden everyone else was really smart and I had to step it up. I focused a lot more on my studies and had to work long and hard at getting good grades. Studying became a priority, but while working on my BS degree, I still had time to enjoy the glamour of Westwood, date my future husband and work enough hours to pay my rent and tuition. I thought then that getting my degree in kinesiology was tough. PA school made all that seem like a cake walk. That is when school became my full-time commitment and there was little time for anything else.

The PA Competencies Online Center[5] gives a detailed listing of all of the skills which PAs are expected to acquire during school and maintain throughout their careers. I have reprinted the "Competencies for the Physician Assistant Profession" in the appendix and I encourage you to review this brief document to help you better understand the expectations of PA students.

Once enrolled in the PA program, you will get to know ALL of your classmates at least as well as you know your college roommate. You will attend lectures and workshops all day and gather for study groups at night. You will "examine" one another, give each other injections and draw each other's blood. You will excel in hematology and struggle in orthopedics. You will learn from lectures and discussion groups from PAs, physicians, dieticians, physical therapists and psychologists. And, you will learn from the experience of your classmates. You will rely on each other as you work as a team to develop a differential diagnosis. You will make flash cards and graphs and stay up all night until the Krebs cycle spins on its own. You will learn together and you will grow together. And that is just the first year!

Clinical rotations take you on the next whirlwind of experiences, during the second half of the PA program. Every program is a little different, but the premise is the same. You are on a "rotation" for about 4 weeks. You are part of a team that includes an attending physician, resident physicians, intern physicians, and maybe a PA or another PA student. Many rotations are at the hospital and often you find your shifts scheduled during hours you previously thought only 7-Eleven® clerks worked. You eat at the hospital cafeteria when you get a chance. You grab a nap on a hospital

---

5   http://www.nccpa.net/PAC/Competencies_home.aspx

bed when your pager isn't calling. You feel like a sponge trying to soak in all the information you can while trying to remember what you learned during the didactic session on anemia so you can use that knowledge on a real patient. You are caught between providing the patient with care and learning everything there is to know about their disease. And, just as you think you are finally getting it, your rotation is over and you start again with a different team in a different specialty.

Rotations can be inpatient (hospital-based) or outpatient (based at an office). Specialties include family practice, pediatrics, geriatrics, internal medicine, obstetrics and gynecology, emergency medicine, psychiatry, orthopedics, general surgery, surgical subspecialties, and medical subspecialties. This is true exposure to what PA life is like. You will learn more while diagnosing one patient with leukemia than you did after reading about cancer for a whole month the year prior. You learn to apply your knowledge and how to learn from patients as well as from your preceptors. You will see patients with very common disorders and you will see cases of rare diagnoses that you will want to share with your colleagues so that they can learn, too. You will learn about yourself and whether you love the excitement of the ER or the consistency of a subspecialty clinic. If you know that you are particularly interested in one specialty area, most programs provide the flexibility to do additional rotations in that field. Amazingly, in the end, you have gathered enough knowledge about medicine and about providing care in a team model to perform effectively as a PA. You are now ready to take the national certification boards!

What are "the Boards"?

The National Commission on Certification of Physician Assistants (NCCPA)[6] is the organization that develops and maintains the initial and recertification board examinations for PAs. You will want to familiarize yourself with their website at www.nccpa.net. The PANCE, or Physician Assistant National Certifying Exam is the exam that is required for initial licensure as a PA in every state. Therefore, to practice as a PA in the United States, you must first graduate from an accredited program and then pass the PANCE. After successfully passing the exam, you are entitled to use

---

6   http://www.nccpa.net/

the designation PA-C, where "C" stands for certified. The NCCPA also administers the PANRE, or Physician Assistant National Recertification Examination, which is taken every 6 years in order to maintain national certification.

By the time you are ready to study for the initial certifying boards you will be overwhelmed with the resources to help you. There are on-line programs, lecture programs, books and independent study programs. Talk to a few different PAs who have just passed the exam to see what helped them. You will probably meet some students in the class just ahead of yours at your program and they will be graduating when you are finishing your first year. Stay in touch with a couple of these students. They often can give you pointers about what they felt helped them. They can direct you to resources. They cannot and will not, however, share with you any specific questions. We all sign an agreement to that affect when we take the exam. You should never put a PA in the position of feeling like they should share specific content of the exam – they can lose their certification over it and it is not worth it!

Also try to find a PA that DIDN'T pass the boards. You may learn even more from that person. Find out what they learned about themselves and what they would do differently to prepare for their second attempt at taking the boards.

You will have to consider how you learn best and be sure to set a schedule to study so you stay on track. The NCCPA offers a practice test or self-assessment that you are eligible to take after you have signed up for the certification exam. The actual exam is 360 questions in a multiple choice format. The tests are administered at computer facilities across the country. You will want to sign up as soon as you are eligible to get a date at a convenient location.

Residency Programs

You will hear about residency, fellowship or postgraduate programs. These programs are for PAs who have completed a PA program and are looking for additional training in a specialty field. They are not mandatory for employment in most cases, although some employers may prefer that you have completed this type of intensive additional training. PAs can apply to a residency program just out of PA school or after years of practice. The organization that assists in the development of postgraduate programs is the Association of Postgraduate Physician Assistant Programs (APPAP)[7]. The majority of the programs are surgical and subspecialty surgical programs which focus on preparing the graduate PA to work as a first assist in surgery. There are also programs that prepare you to work in critical care, dermatology, emergency medicine, hospitalist medicine, neonatology, ob-gyn, oncology, psychiatry, rheumatology, sleep medicine, trauma and urology. Most of the programs are a full year in length and pay the PA a stipend during the training. I spoke with Lisa Rotellini-Coltvet, MA, MMS, PA-C who is the President of the APPAP, and she had this to say about postgraduate training:

> *Although postgraduate training is not for everyone, it provides opportunity for those who desire experience in and exposure to specialty medicine in a unique manner. Employment opportunities and roles for PAs are rapidly expanding to include a high proportion of specialty areas. Because of the diversity and specialization of PAs, formal postgraduate training is assuming a greater importance as an adjunct to PA primary care education. Postgraduate curriculums are designed to build upon the knowledge and experience acquired in PA school enabling the PA to competently assume a role as a physician assistant on a specialty health care team. Many postgraduate programs have pioneered the role of the PA in these specialty areas and offer experienced role models as well as formalized instruction.*

> *Residency programs and other types of postgraduate specialty training provide very intense, organized educational programming that offers the participants a wide variety of experiences in a short period of time. Most residency programs can be completed in twelve months while some require a longer time frame. In a short period of time you are able to develop confidence and experience that would otherwise have taken years to attain. This*

---

7   http://www.appap.org

experience will make you a much more attractive candidate to an employer and, hopefully, allow you to start your career with a higher level of responsibility and salary. Additionally, if you are an experienced physician assistant, it may provide opportunity for you to change specialty areas or to significantly advance your skills and knowledge in your current employment.

If you are considering postgraduate education, ask yourself the following questions:

- *Why should I attend a residency program or any other type of postgraduate program?*

- *Why not just take a job in orthopedics, emergency medicine, primary care, surgery, dermatology, or other specialty area and learn that specialty from an employer?*

- *What advantages will an organized specialty program or residency offer me and how will it help my career?*

If your answers support ongoing academics, specialized training, and exposure to a wide array of experiences, then a postgraduate fellowship/residency may be the perfect opportunity to meet both your personal and professional goals. Regardless, research each program you are considering and talk with graduates from these programs to gain a better sense if it is the right fit for you. Please visit the APPAP (The Association for Postgraduate PA Programs) website (www.appap.org) for a list of programs by specialty and information about postgraduate training.

Are you overwhelmed now? It sounds like a lot of work because it is. This career path should not be taken lightly. It is tough, but manageable. Heck, about 80,000 of us have done it! The good news, too, is that few fail once accepted into a school. If you get into a program, usually it is because you belong there. The programs are very good at identifying students who will graduate, pass the boards, and succeed. They don't want to use up space in the class with someone who really wants to be a doctor, or someone that cannot succeed as a PA. So, once you are accepted, you will work hard, but you have made it there because you are supposed to be there. So, make us all proud and give it your full attention.

Who's the Boss?

There will a job out there for you when you graduate. You can move anywhere in the country and probably find a job. That feels good to know. But, you probably won't get your ideal job right out of school. Bummer! Don't get me wrong – there are plenty of PAs who started working right out of school and years later are still working with the same physician and loving it. You might have to move or commute further than you would like. You may even need to take a position in a specialty that isn't your first choice. But, you can find a job. And sometimes the job you take becomes your ideal situation even when you aren't expecting it!

The good news is that you can work in any field of medicine, as long as you are in partnership with a physician. State law can restrict your practice. I will say it again many times in this book…be sure to look at your state laws and regulations because they differ throughout the country. In general, though, PAs work with MDs (Medical Doctors) or DOs (Doctor of Osteopathy) in most fields of medicine. The 2008 AAPA census data tells us that 37% of PAs work in primary care settings. These are considered to be family/general practice, pediatrics, general internal medicine and ob/gyn. Amazingly, your day can be very different if you are in family practice compared with a PA in cardiovascular surgery. But, your salary should match the intensity level and long hours with which you may be faced. The last half of this chapter is filled with real life stories of what a day is like for a PA in different specialty settings. I think when you get a feel for the types of patients you can see, and the variety (or lack of variety) of the diagnoses, you will start to get a feel for the type of practice that will match your lifestyle and interests. But, that could change once you are in school, too!

THE NUMBER ONE MOST IMPORTANT FACTOR IN YOUR EMPLOYMENT IS YOUR SUPERVISING PHYSICIAN. Let me say it again. The NUMBER ONE most important factor in your employment is your supervising physician. I don't repeat myself often, but this is SO important and I speak from personal experience. Don't take this lightly, please. Your job as a PA is more than a job. It is a career. When you are looking to take a job, consider that it may be your last, really. You should treat it like a long-term relationship, a commitment, a marriage. In fact, I encourage new PAs to "date" their new job first before making that commitment. That doesn't mean bringing in roses or chocolate (although that might get your foot in the door!), it means trying it out. The best advice I ever received after my first (disastrous) job was to "shadow" the physician before you accept a position with her. I have never heard of a physician not loving this idea. I thought it was a unique suggestion, but came to find out there is a whole Job Shadow Coalition[1]. There is even a National Job Shadow Day! Who knew? So, it is recommended in other professions as well that before you sign on the dotted line, ask if you can spend a day in the office or whatever setting you will be in. You won't be able to see patients or write in the charts. You just want to follow the doctor around to see what it is like. You learn A LOT! Not only do you learn about the doctors and how the patients respond to them, you learn about the staff, the administration, the stress level in the office, and what everyone does for lunch. In a single day, you should be able to decide if this is somewhere you can live and someone you can live with. If not, ask to come back again to make sure. You are not going to get there and change the office any more than you are going to start a relationship and change the guy or gal you are dating. So decide right there if you fit in and if it is a good fit for you. If not, keep looking or recognize that it will be temporary.

Who can I work for?

In today's chaos of a medical system we find ourselves in the middle of a web of providers, insurers and patients. There is a legend about a "traditional office" out there – I've never seen one, but I've been told they exist. I think it is what a lot of people still think of as a doctor's office – a small place that looks a little like a very clean house. The physician owns the building and manages the medical assistant and the smiling front office receptionist with her paper appointment book. He sees a patient that he has known since he delivered him 15 years prior – and he sees that patient's mom, brother and uncle, too - and the patient pays him for those services before he leaves the

---

1   http://www.jobshadow.org

office. He writes prescriptions on a prescription pad, not a computer, and his patient just takes the prescription to the pharmacy and fills it without questions. Heck, he may even do house calls! Oh, it all sounds so lovely!! But, back to the 21st century.

You may be hired by a solo physician, but usually there is more to it than that. Often times your employer is actually the medical group in which the physician is a partner. Medical groups benefit you since they make a few small companies into a big company. Suddenly your benefits improve – health insurance for you and your family, 401K and paid time off are much more affordable for that doctor to offer you because the medical group is able to negotiate better rates with the larger numbers. And, now you are working for a larger company. This company may or may not be well-managed or making much of a profit. They may have a billing department that doesn't go after ignored claims or they may be experts at reimbursement. The physicians may be very involved and making most of the decisions, or those decisions may be made in great part by business people. I haven't decided which is better! It is very difficult to assess the success of the company during an interview or even within the early months or years of employment. As a PA employee you may or may not be asked to participate in all of the business decisions for the practice.

You may be hired by a managed care company. I have spoken with PAs employed by large health maintenance organizations that will never leave. They seem secure in the job, work specific hours and enjoy good benefits. You may even have a union that you join. You may need that security and the great benefits. But, you may not have as much to say about the physician you work with or some of the policies that need to be followed.

You may be employed by a hospital. One growing field for PAs is being a hospitalist. There have been recent changes in this area, as there are new restrictions on work hours for physicians in training. Due to those new restrictions, some hospitals had no choice but to hire additional physicians or PAs to cover the hospital in place of the residents that were working too many hours. Many family practice and even internal medicine physicians with private offices no longer do any hospital work. Instead, hospitals have physicians, resident physicians and PAs that take care of the patients while they are in the hospital and then discharge them back to their primary care physician after the acute episodic hospitalization. Some hospitals employ their own hospitalist team and some contract with a physician group.

You may be employed by a physician assistant program. Remember, we need PAs to teach PAs. Many PA educators work full-time in the classroom and take shifts in a clinical setting to keep up their patient skills. Some are involved in clinical or professional research. If you like to teach but don't want to do that full-time, talk with someone at the local PA program about part-time teaching opportunities. Perhaps you can lecture to students about a topic in your specialty or help with workshops.

What about the government? Sure! PAs are employed by State, Local and Federal Government agencies in the Veteran's Administration, the military, correctional facilities, hospitals, community health centers and universities or colleges.

Full-time vs. Part-time

Like physicians, many PAs are finding that part-time employment is right for them. Female PAs who start raising a family may feel the need to be home more. Or, if the PA is the second wage-earner in the family, he/she may be able to afford to only work part-time. But, if your schedule is too restricted this can be difficult, as many jobs require long hours and no guarantee that you won't have to stay overtime to complete a case. This is especially true in some of the ER settings and surgical settings. Are there part-time jobs available? Some physicians find that they are ready to hire a PA, but aren't ready to financially risk hiring someone full-time. They may hire hourly and part-time PAs until the practice grows more, and then offer full-time status. If your hours are more flexible, some PAs find that working part-time in an urgent-care or ER fast-track is an option.

Can I own my own practice?

A small number of PAs across the country own a practice in partnership with a physician. You *must* understand the state laws regarding medical practice ownership where you live. This is generally an area that most PAs do not venture into until they have a lot of clinical experience and at least some business expertise. I won't go further into this topic in this publication except to advise you to do your research and get some help before you consider owning your own practice. To be honest, one of the things that I love most about being a PA is NOT having my own practice and not having to deal with the headaches of personnel, overhead expenses and administration. I like being an employee and spending the majority of my day handling the many stresses of patient care without dealing with running a business as well. But, if you are up for the challenge and do your homework, you should be able to take part ownership in a practice.

What is it really like to work in different specialties?
 Like I said before, you may not land your "ideal" job initially, so you have to keep your mind open. I suspect a lot of PAs working in specialty offices did not set out to find these jobs. Some PAs go to school knowing they will work in cardiovascular surgery or cannot imagine themselves in any place other than pediatrics. That is great to have the ambition and to have a goal in mind. But, I bet if you ask most PAs who are in specialty areas today, most just had an opportunity and took it. They weren't really sure if it was the right thing, but they tried it out and liked it. Part of the decision that drives your practice choice may be the current demand in your demographic area. Now that PAs are in most specialties, there really is nothing to keep you from finding that job that you know you want.

Remember that family practice is a specialty as well. Even though PAs are being hired into all fields of medicine, let's not forgot the importance and significance of primary care. As the population ages and we all continue to live longer, the need for primary care providers increases. Meanwhile, the numbers of physicians going into non-primary care specialty practice increases. Unfortunately, this is a dangerous trend that may leave us with a significant access to care issue very soon. If all PAs that graduated from a PA program from now on all stayed in primary care, we would probably just barely make a dent in the problem of getting preventative and basic services to all Americans. Think about the roots of the profession. We were bread to fill a void – to address the concern of a physician shortage. Consider where the shortage is, or is going to be, when making your career choice. Where can you make the most impact? What can you handle? What will you be satisfied doing? I've had a couple different specialty PAs tell me how much they respect my staying in Family Practice. "I could never do that," they say. Seems so basic right out of school – you just have to know all of it! You do have to keep up on the knowledge in many different areas, and you never really feel like an "expert" in anything. But like all other specialty areas, there are challenges and rewards.

Who is not driven by money? Maybe you have plenty of it, but for many of us, we are motivated to bring in a good income with this profession. Maybe that is the reason you are reading this book - physician assistants make a good salary. It stands to reason that our salaries sort of mirror the salaries of physicians – family practice and pediatrics tend to be on the lower end of the salary range and surgical subspecialties are on the higher end. But the slope is much steeper for physicians. A surgeon may triple or quadruple (or more!) the salary of a pediatrician, but a PA working in surgery may only make 50% more than a primary care PA in the same demographic area with a similar amount of experience. The AAPA publishes a census annually and reports for 2008, the average income for full-time PAs among all specialties is just shy of $90,000 and among new graduates is about $76,000.

As you read through the following, I hope you get a little flavor for the different settings. I am going to start with my own personal experience as a family practice PA (only because I can, because it is my book!), then you will get to enjoy the submissions from PAs in different specialties. It is not meant to be an exhaustive list. My intent is to give you a flavor for what different PAs do in different settings. But, as much as there are many different specialties, there are different types of work that PAs do within a specialty. So, keep in mind that there are certainly variations on the theme and this is just a taste of the types of opportunities out there.

There really is no "typical day" for any of us. We are faced with using our knowledge to help diagnose and treat the patient in the examining room. And, that can be straight-forward and routine or it can involve a significant medical history and multiple medical and social factors. I am sure that when I asked the PA contributors below for an accounting of a typical day, most of them had a little difficulty explaining exactly what that is. Hopefully, this allows you to peek at the life of a PA in different settings. I have also included the website that will link you to the AAPA Specialty Organization that can give you more information about that field of medicine for PAs, but that does not mean to imply that the Specialty Organization necessarily approved the submission.

Family Practice
Association of Family Practice Physician Assistants
(www.afppa.org)
Submitted by Beth Grivett, PA-C

I work in a large group family practice with eight physicians, two nurse practitioners and myself. I was hired to work 32 hours per week which is nice for me because it gives me a little more family time. I used to take a full day off, but now I work shorter days which I like better for now. So, my day starts at 9:00 a.m. and I usually do not have a full schedule when I walk in the door. Our schedulers are very good at predicting how much to "pre-fill" my schedule with physicals and follow-up appointments and how much to leave open for same day appointments. A lot of it has to do with physician vacations, how busy the "on-call" doctor is and past experience for the time of the year.

Most days I will do 3-6 adult physicals in a day for which they schedule 30 minutes. During these appointments, I will perform a complete physical exam including pap smear or prostate check and order all age and gender appropriate screening tests including EKG, blood testing, mammogram, dexa/bone density test and an evaluation for colonoscopy. I will update immunizations and medications. Additionally, I address all the chronic conditions for which the patient is seeing us and get an update on diagnoses for which they have been referred out to specialists. I address general health including tobacco use, drug and alcohol use, exercise, safety and recommended supplements and I assess the patient's mental health. I try to make recommendations about just one or two things that the patient should start working on. I have found there is a fine line between addressing too much and trying to "fix" everything and overwhelming the patient. We will see them again soon, so I don't feel compelled to give them too much to work on all at once. Oh, and I also have to answer the questions they bring in, often in grocery list form, which they have been "saving up" to ask!

The rest of my day is filled with all the other stuff. I see a lot of people who call the same day, or the day prior, to be seen for more urgent needs including rashes, coughs and colds, sprains and strains, back pain, infections of just about anywhere, depression, anxiety, chest pain, abdominal pain, bladder infections, vaginal infections, headache, etc. I also see patients in need of follow-up care for their chronic condition(s). Seems there is hardly ever just one issue, but some combination of diabetes, hypertension, heart disease, renal or liver disease, hyperlipidemia (high cholesterol), dementia, headache, depression, anxiety, hyper/hypothyroid, menopause, arthritis, chronic pain, etc.

In my practice I do not do a lot of procedures. I will sew up a laceration if the patient comes in instead of going to the ER and I will perform skin biopsies and do an incision and drainage of an abscess or cyst, but that is about it.

I work with all of the physicians in my practice. I love the fact that we all do our charting in one big room because we can all just throw out general questions and see who will answer them. That is so much easier than looking something up in a book or on-line. I will consult with the primary doctor for a patient or with the on-call doctor while the patient waits, if there is a difficult case, if I am considering sending a patient to the ER, or if I just sense that the patient would feel more comfortable knowing that his doctor was involved immediately. I will also bring the doctor into the room with me to listen to a heart murmur or to verify my exam of the patient about once a week. We have gotten very good at depending on one another for dermatologic conditions and jokingly call it "derm by committee" when we sometimes bring in 1-2 other providers to verify an unusual rash. Within about the first year of employment, I believe I earned the respect of the physicians with whom I work. They now completely trust me to take good care of their patients and know I will seek their consult when appropriate.

Addiction Medicine Society of Physician Assistants in Addiction Medicine
(www.spaam.net)

Submitted by Bernard Stuetz, PA-C, MA, President of the Society of PAs in Addiction Medicine

The specialty of addiction medicine includes knowledge of the addiction process including the physical damage to the human body and the social, psychological and spiritual aspects of addiction. This includes close utilization of the 12-step recovery program. The knowledge of internal medicine is an integral part of addiction medicine.

I see all the new patients that have been admitted during the night. I report to my supervising psychiatrist the main problem cases he needs to know about. I then round on the other patients, who had been previously hospitalized, to chart their progress. The main cases I treat are all kinds of drug dependence including opiate, cocaine, benzodiazepine, marijuana, alcohol and hallucinogens. I also treat psychiatric illness including major depression, schizophrenia, bipolar disorder, attention deficient disorder, anger management disorder, and social functioning disorders.

The biggest struggle facing our specialty is the recognition of PAs by the American Society of Addiction Medicine and the American Psychiatric Association-Addiction Psychiatric section. If there was more support, we could make huge inroads into patient care nationally. Secondly, this acknowledgement would make it easier for us to be recognized by all insurance companies as credentialed health care providers under state insurance plans. This would allow us to bill the state or local government agency for our services. Proper reimbursement would increase our value and patient access to care. However, proper reimbursement requires that each state's Medicaid plan specifically states in regulations that we can examine, diagnose and treat all patients under the guidance of our supervising physician and within the scope of practice under state laws.

Allergy and Immunology
American Academy of Physician Assistants in Allergy,
Asthma and Immunology
(www.aapa-aai.com)
Submitted by Gabriel Ortiz, MPAS, PA-C, DFAAPA,
AAPA Liaison to American Academy of Allergy Asthma
Immunology (AAAAI), AAAAI Liaison to AAPA

My sub-specialty is pediatric pulmonary/allergy. I usually see about 25-30 patients a day with well controlled and/or acute allergy and asthma. A few patients may need to be admitted to the hospital for continuous oxygen therapy and nebulized albuterol. If I see a patient who needs to be admitted to the hospital, I will consult my supervising physician to see if there is anything else that we can do in the office beforehand. My patient load mostly includes asthma and allergies and I see some patients with cystic fibrosis. If there are any changes to be made with the routine medications for the cystic fibrosis patients these changes will be approved by my supervising physician. A few of my patients are also ventilator dependent.

I think the biggest struggle for us may be the decreased reimbursement for immunotherapy (allergy vaccinations). We also have an increasing problem with reimbursement for specialty care for our Medicaid patients due to the current State Children's Health Insurance Program (SCHIP) reimbursement being lower than what would be considered adequate.

Cardiovascular Surgery
Association of Physician Assistants in Cardiovascular Surgery
(www.apacvs.org)
Submitted by Doug Condit, PA-C, Editor, Association of
Physician Assistants in Cardiovascular Surgery (APACVS)

At 6:30 a.m., four PAs enter the PA office on the cardiac telemetry unit in a major medical center. These PAs will be providing the 'primary' minute-to-minute care of the patients on the cardiothoracic surgery service for the next 12 hours. Patients on the service include all those patients who are recovering from cardiothoracic surgery and those who will be going to surgery in the near future. Cardiothoracic patients include those with coronary artery disease, valvular heart disease, cardiac myopathies and congenital heart disease. They may have recently undergone coronary artery revascularization, repair or replacement of one of their heart valves, surgical reconstruction of their heart, repair of their intra-thoracic aorta, repair of a congenital defect, placement of a left-ventricular assist device, or a heart transplant. Each of these conditions requires similar but different postoperative care. In addition to patients with cardiac disease, the cardiothoracic surgical service is also responsible for patients recovering from thoracic surgery, including surgery of their lungs, trachea, esophagus, diaphragm, and/or mediastinum.

The PA who was covering the patients overnight presents each of the PAs with a list of all the patients on the cardiothoracic service and those who are on other services but are active consults of the cardiothoracic service. He then presents a brief medical summary of each patient to the oncoming PAs. This 'hand-off' of patients is one of the most important parts of a hospital-based PA, no matter what service the PA is on. During this time period, the oncoming PA has an opportunity to familiarize themselves with the patient, although the PA may not yet have physically met that patient.

Following this 'hand-off' of patients, the oncoming PAs examine those patients for whom they will be providing the care. Prior to seeing each patient, the PA reviews and charts the patient's current vital signs and their intake and output. The PA then performs a comprehensive physical examination of each patient. While the examination has at its focus the function of the organ(s) which required surgery, it also encompasses the entire patient. Although the patient has recently had a surgical procedure, the PA cannot neglect any other body functions, as the patient is an entire human, not merely 'the valve patient.'

At 8:00 a.m., ninety minutes after the PAs have begun their day, one or more attending cardiothoracic surgeons arrive on the telemetry unit. Each PA presents a synopsis of each individual patient to the surgeon(s), including any abnormalities noted and any concerns. The surgeon(s) then examine any areas of concern of each patient and the surgeon(s) and PAs formulate a plan for the care of the patient for the day.

Following the attending rounds, the PAs then meet with the physical therapists, occupational therapists, nursing care manager and social worker. During this session, they discuss each patients' physical progress postoperatively, any special needs they may have following discharge and what an appropriate, safe discharge would be for each individual patient. While the ideal situation would be for each patient to return to their home in a timely fashion, this is not reality. Each patient is an individual and recovers at a different rate. Also, each patient has different co-morbidities, which may impact their rate of recovery. Consequently, to expedite their recovery, some patients would do better at an acute rehabilitation facility while others would be better served by going to a subacute rehabilitation facility. Once each patient has been reviewed in this multi-disciplinary meeting, the nursing care manager interacts with each patient's nurse to coordinate care and the social worker not only addresses each patient's psychosocial needs, but also works toward securing them a safe discharge.

After establishing the plan of care for each patient, each PA then returns to the patients she or he is responsible for during their 12 hour shift. They remove any unnecessary hardware (e.g. chest tubes inserted during surgery, which are no longer needed; temporary pacemaker wires, implanted during surgery, to be used, if necessary, to regulate the patients heart rate during their early post-operative course; central intravenous lines, etc.). The PA then places any necessary consultations with other specialty services. For example, if the patient begins developing abnormalities in the laboratory values relating to their kidneys, the PA may seek consultation from the kidney (renal medicine) service.

By mid-morning, the daily laboratory results are available on the hospital's computer system and the PA reviews the values for each of her/his patients. Sometimes the PA must order supplements of various electrolytes in individual patients. Other times they may note an increase or decrease in specific laboratory values, which show the development of potential problems. When such abnormalities are detected, the PA takes appropriate action.

The PA then prepares for the discharge of any patient leaving that day. The discharge process requires the PA to prepare a discharge summary on every patient leaving the hospital, whether they are going home or to a rehabilitation facility. Patients who are being discharged home also have to have prescriptions generated for each of the medications he/she will be taking.

During the day, one of the PAs on the cardiothoracic service carries the consult beeper. She or he is responsible for responding to all of the consults referred to the cardiothoracic team during the day. These consults may come from the emergency department, the cardiac catheterization laboratory, or the medical service. She/he is the first member of the cardiothoracic service to see and evaluate each patient. Depending on the severity/urgency of the consult, she/he may phone a senior PA, a cardiothoracic fellow or an attending surgeon.

In addition, PAs admit patients to the service. During the admission process, they perform a complete history and physical examination, place orders for admission laboratory examinations, order medications, order a diet and place orders for any nursing care the patient requires, including vital signs, weights, intake and output, activity limitations, etc.

The PAs also perform preoperative assessments of patients scheduled for the operating room in the near future. This includes performing a physical assessment of the patient, reviewing of all their laboratory results, and assuring that the blood bank has received a 'type and crossmatch' specimen on the patient. The PA performs an intra-oral examination on all patients who are going to have an artificial device implanted within their cardiovascular system (such as an artificial heart valve) and request a dental evaluation on any patient who appears to have periodontal disease.

At 6:30 a.m., when there are four PAs reporting to the PA office on the telemetry unit, there are also PAs reporting to the operating room. The cardiothoracic surgery PA plays an integral role in the majority of cardiothoracic surgical procedures performed.

Before the patient arrives in the operating room, the cardiothoracic PA reviews the pre-operative checklist previously filled in by one of the "floor PAs." (I put that term in quotations, as the majority of cardiothoracic PAs work both inside and outside of the O.R.). She/he checks the form for completeness and notes any abnormalities outlined in the checklist. While the anesthesiologists are inducing anesthesia, the PA positions the patient and inserts a catheter into the patient's bladder. After the patient is asleep, the PA then scrubs the patient with an antiseptic soap and/or alcohol and drapes the patient to aid in the prevention of infection.

When the procedure begins, the cardiothoracic PA performs as the first and/or second assistant during the procedure. If the patient is undergoing coronary arterial revascularization, the PA will often harvest the saphenous vein, which will be used as a conduit to bring a new blood supply to the patient's heart. Today, most saphenous veins are harvested using an endovascular technique, whereby the PA makes a small incision near the patient's knee, then inserts a telescopic type of instrument through the incision and removes the saphenous vein through this single, small incision.

After the procedure is over, which may take from one to several hours, the PA then accompanies the patient to the intensive care unit. In the unit, the PA discusses the patient in depth with the nurse and the ICU PA who will be providing the immediate care for the patient. The PA also writes a brief operative note, which gives an overview of what procedure(s) were performed on the patient. The PA then enters all of the patient's postoperative orders into the hospitals computer system.

Dermatology
Society of Dermatology Physician Assistants
(www.dermpa.org) (www.dermcast.tv)
Submitted by Robert Higham, MPAS, PA-C

My typical day starts around 8:00 a.m. I begin by reviewing the prior days' laboratory reports and begin on patient phone calls that might have come in during the evening hours. My first patient is scheduled at 8:30 a.m. and I will work throughout the morning until noon. I generally have time to take a lunch for about an hour. My afternoon patients begin at 1:15 p.m. and continue until 4:45 p.m. I currently work Monday through Friday and do not work on the weekends. In dermatology, typically each of the providers in the office takes their own patient call, unlike many other specialties of medicine; dermatology typically has an extremely low after-hours call volume. In a typical day, I might see an average of 30 to 34 patients. General dermatology encompasses approximately 70% of my practice with about 30% of my practice being in cosmetics. In our office we meet biweekly as a management team to discuss the practice and address any management or office related issues that might arise. In addition to the biweekly management meetings, we meet regularly with our front and back office staff on alternating weeks to discuss their department's issues and concerns and address any issues that need to be dealt with. By interacting with both the management and clerical staff on a regular basis, our office is able to address issues rapidly and work at its maximum efficiency.

General dermatology patients present with a number of common problems. Most often we see patients seeking care for acne, rashes, skin cancers and precancerous growths, changing moles, warts and other benign skin growths. Many of the problems in dermatology can be treated in one to two visits. However, a number of common conditions that we treat such as acne, psoriasis or eczema, require regular visits to the office until the conditions are stabilized, at which point regular routine follow up visits can be made at the appropriate time interval. One of the most common presenting problems we see is the patient who is concerned about changing moles and skin growths. As we continue to see an increasing aging population and, unfortunately, continue to see patients who expose themselves to large amounts of artificial (indoor tanning) and natural (outdoor) sunlight, the issues of precancerous and cancerous growths remain high on our list of daily activities. On any given day we might biopsy five or ten lesions on multiple patients with a large percentage of them being skin cancers. There are a number of skin cancers that can present in dermatology, including basal cell epitheliomas, squamous cell carcinomas and melanomas.

Throughout the day a number of cosmetic dermatologic patients might be seen in our office. Typically these patients are presenting for improvement of fine lines, wrinkles, photoaging and correction of superficial blood vessels. In addition, patients also frequently access our dermatology office for the removal of unwanted hair. The patients might be treated with multiple injectable medications including Botox ® (botulinum A toxin) and Hyaluronic acid fillers including Restylane®, Perlane®, Juvéderm®, etc. There are many laser and light-based devices utilized in our dermatology practice treating everything from unwanted facial hair to brown spots on the face and hands. In addition, lasers are used to eliminate unwanted blood vessels both on the face and other areas on the body, especially the legs. Cosmetic dermatology continues to increase, in our practice and across America. I find it incredibly important to maintain an appropriate balance in my daily schedule between medical and cosmetic dermatology patients.

In our practice, PAs have an independent schedule just like our physician colleagues in our office. It is our office policy to introduce new patients to the office to our physicians within the first or second visit. In addition, we have the ability to discuss clinical issues as needed throughout the day. This ability to consult with the physicians in our office regarding patients I might see provides an invaluable learning experience and increased level of care for our patients. It is very important, in my opinion, to have access to your supervising physician as needed throughout the normal day, as clinical issues might arise. Typically, as PAs become more experienced in dermatology, like in all areas of specialty practice, the amount of interaction on a daily basis with the supervising physicians typically decreases to the point of interacting with only the most difficult or unusual cases, which need both the physician and PA interaction.

In dermatology, one may face a number of challenging issues. The biggest issue seems to be the ability of patients to access timely care. There is a great shortage particularly of rural dermatologists within America. There are areas in the country where a typical wait time for an appointment can be anywhere from six to eight weeks for a new patient. There are a number of reasons for this backlog of patients, including the aging patient population, the surge of cosmetic dermatology, and a large number of female dermatologists who may work fewer days and/or fewer hours than their male counterparts. Fortunately dermatology PAs are well positioned to increase access to patient care in dermatology practices, as they primarily see the general dermatology patients.

Endocrinology
American Society of Endocrine Physician Assistants
(www.endocrine-pa.com)
Submitted by Scott Urquhart PA-C, President, American Society of Endocrine PAs (ASEPA); Adjunct Clinical Professor, James Madison University Physician Assistant Program; Clinical Instructor, George Washington University Physician Assistant Program; Clinical PA-C, Diabetes and Thyroid Associates, Fredericksburg, VA.

My usual day is full-time outpatient endocrine care. I spend my day seeing new patient consultations and follow-up patients. My time slots are 15 minutes for all follow-up visits for endocrine diseases and 30 minutes for all new patient consults with the exception of a new diabetic patient, who is allocated 45 minutes. A day full of follow-up cases would account for 24 visits. I see and treat all endocrine diseases except for those involving reproductive endocrinology. My supervising physician is a board certified endocrinologist. With regards to how we handle patient flow and visits, we see the same types of patients. Caring for and sharing the same patients, we function as an endocrine team with a fine ability to provide an outstanding continuity of care. Throughout my day, I am continually addressing labs, patient call-in concerns, and making medication adjustments on patients' blood sugars that have been faxed to our office. This "inbox" if you will, never seems to get emptied! My lunch time and time immediately after seeing daily patients is spent running the American Society of Endocrine Physician Assistants (ASEPA), for which I am President. Some of this time is spent in development of educational programs for which I am involved in lecturing at State and National PA meetings.

After having hospital privileges for 6 years on the inpatient endocrine service we transitioned to outpatient care 6 years ago. This change has afforded me a better quality of life working Monday through Thursdays and half days on Fridays with no call or weekend responsibilities.

I see patients with type 1 and type 2 diabetes, hypertension, dyslipidemia, metabolic syndrome, obesity, all types of thyroid disorders, thyroid cancer, osteoporosis, polycystic ovarian syndrome, male hypogonadism, vitamin D deficiency, Paget's disease, adrenal disorders, pituitary disorders and tumors and more.

The biggest struggle or burden in our specialty is the nationwide shortage of board certified endocrinologists. This shortage is expected to worsen in the years to come as we are seeing fewer and fewer internists entering endocrine fellowships. One of the missions of ASEPA is to increase awareness of the specialty and encourage our PA colleagues to consider this rewarding specialty. We have been working closely with the American Association of Clinical Endocrinologists over the years to partner-up and find ways and means to ensure that the US will continue to address this shortage. With the continual increase in the new diagnosis of diabetes patients and our older population of patients developing osteoporosis for example, we need to stay ahead of the curve.

Gastroenterology
Gastroenterology Physician Assistants
(www.gipas.org)
Submitted by Douglas L. Senecal, PA-C, MPAS, President, Gastroenterology Physician Assistants

My first experience with being a gastroenterology (GI) physician assistant was in private practice where I would start my day by rounding on the hospital patients, completing a focused exam and reviewing and ordering labs or studies. I would then rendezvous with my attending physician to discuss any details that were outside of my level of experience or knowledge. From that point I would make my way to clinic where I would see a diverse population of patients both new and established. I, along with another PA, was essentially the first line of care in screening patients who would later go on to have endoscopy or following up with those who had had procedures and were returning for discussion of results. I went on from my practice in GI to do an advanced fellowship in Hepatology and now work at a transplant center where I manage patients with end-stage liver disease, both inpatient and outpatient, and first assist on all liver transplant surgeries. So, as you can see, the specialty pathway can be quite diverse and most often rewarding.

In a gastroenterology practice, you will see diagnoses including acute and chronic pancreatitis, pancreatic cancer, gastroesophageal reflux disease, barrett's esophagus, esophagitis, acute and chronic viral hepatitis, cirrhosis, liver cancer, ascites, cholecystitis, ulcerative colitis, crohn's disease, constipation, infectious and non-infectious diarrhea, irritable bowel disease, colon cancer screening, etc.

In some instances my supervising physician and I see complex cases together; in others, I act as a quasi-independent provider and utilize my supervising physician on a consultant basis so he can best utilize his higher skill set such as performing endoscopic intervention and screening.

At this point our biggest struggle as a PA specialty is providing a comprehensive core educational course for those new to the specialty while also serving the continuing educational needs of our peers with state-of-the-art updates. My initial learning curve was tremendous, as instead of a broad primary care approach to my knowledge base I was now to focus on a deep understanding of one specialty. It was difficult to sort out which professional society resources were most appropriate in obtaining my specialty education. In turn, I recommend anybody entering into a specialty seek out the appropriate PA specialty organization for a list of resources. This allows you to call upon the past experience of others.

Geriatrics Society of PAs Caring for the Elderly
www.geri-pa.org
Submitted by Freddi Segal-Gidan, P.A., Ph.D, Founder, Past-President of Society of PAs Caring for the Elderly (SPACE)

I work in geriatrics, which is the care of older people. Most of the patients I see are over age 60, the majority over age 70, many in their 80s and some in their 90s. The oldest patient I ever cared for was 105 when he died. I see patients in the clinic two days per week, and the remainder of my time is devoted to research and administration. When I am in clinic I usually see one or two new patients and then follow up on returning patients. It takes me between 90 minutes and two hours to see a new patient, and 30-45 minutes for returning patients, depending on the situation.

Every patient is accompanied by a family member (or many) during their visit and the family is included throughout the process. Because the patients I see are elderly, they have lots of history and it is often very long and complicated. Even before I see the patient, the nurse has often spoken with the family to obtain background information and the family is provided with a number of forms to complete about the person's function and behavior. In the exam room I speak with the patient first and then with a family member, so I can get both perspectives. Then I examine the patient, starting with a mental status exam that helps me assess their current memory ability and thinking. I watch the patient walk, examine their eyes and ears, listen to their heart and lungs and evaluate their neurologic system. I have every patient I see take off their shoes and socks so I can examine their feet, since this can tell me how well someone is taking care of himself (or being taken care of). I then order any necessary tests to complete my evaluation.

When I see a new patient, I discuss the case briefly with my supervising physician and introduce each new patient and family to her. When she sees new patients she also introduces me to them – that way everyone knows both of us. We participate in case conferences together twice a month and have an opportunity to discuss patients at that time. Otherwise we are usually in different offices, on different campuses, so we communicate by email about reports and research studies or we phone one another. My supervising physician and I have worked together for many years and exemplify a true team approach to patient care. We were honored in 2008 to be awarded the AAPA Paragon Award for Physician-PA PArtnership[2].

When I see returning patients we discuss test results, find out how they are tolerating medication or discuss new problems that have arisen. If a patient is having behavior problems or psychiatric issues I can call on the psychiatrist on our team to see the patient that day or within a short interval. I also work with a social worker who is available to see patients in the clinic and works with the families in locating community services.

I spend some time every day reviewing charts for medication refills, contacting pharmacies to clarify orders, reviewing laboratory test results and returning phone calls from families. I am often called by families of patients we care for when there is a crisis, such as when someone falls and is injured, has wandered away and gotten lost, or when a patient is dying. I speak with the family by phone or meet with them in my office, discuss the situation and help them to decide what course of action is in the best interest of the patient.

In my administrative role I am responsible for writing regular reports on projects and doing grant applications which requires me to spend time every day at the computer writing. I am also usually writing or editing a manuscript for an article or chapter for publication.

---

2   http://www.aapa.org/membership/awards.html

Several times a week I participate in a family meeting along with a social worker, and sometimes other health care providers. A patient and their family, as few or as many members as wish to attend, are all invited to come in and discuss the patient's condition. The meeting usually lasts about an hour. The patient's diagnosis is reviewed, plan for treatment discussed and questions answered.

Twice a month in the afternoon I participate in a case conference where all new patients seen, and occasionally other cases of interest, are reviewed and discussed by the PAs, physicians, psychologists, social workers and others with whom I work. This usually lasts for 2-3 hours. Once or twice a week I attend another meeting involving planning an upcoming conference, preparing for a grant or new research project, or discussing a new initiative at the hospital or university.

Previously my clinical job included caring for older patients on a rehabilitation unit where most had had a stroke or other illness that left them in need of rehabilitation in order to return home. I would work in the hospital half of every day seeing patients, participating in meetings about each patient with the other team members (nurses, therapists, pharmacists and psychologists), teaching and overseeing students assigned to the unit for clerkships and meeting with patients and their families to discuss the patient's condition, treatment plan, and progress. Earlier in my career I also saw patients in nursing homes and did home care, but currently I only see patients in the clinic, and occasionally in the hospital.

The majority of patients I currently see have some kind of dementia (memory problems and other thinking problems). This includes Alzheimer's disease, vascular (multi-infarct) dementia, Lewy body dementia, fronto-temporal dementia and Parkinson's disease. Most of the patients I see also have other chronic medical problems such as hypertension, diabetes, thyroid disease, arthritis, heart disease and hearing loss.

There is certainly a disconnect between the payment allowed by insurance companies and other payors and the time it takes to take care of elderly people with long and complicated histories who have multiple medical problems and long lists of medications than can interact. Geriatrics is not seen as a highly desirable specialty in medicine and struggles for recognition. With the aging of the population there is a growing need for health professionals with training and expertise in caring for older people.

Nephrology
American Academy of Nephrology Physician Assistants (www.aanpa.org)
Submitted by Kim Zuber, PAC, MSPS, Vice President of the American Academy of Nephrology PAs, Chair of the Council of Advanced Practitioners/National Kidney Foundation

Nephrology is not the 'sexy' discipline that you dream about in PA school but it is the most family-friendly specialty I have found. There are many more jobs in nephrology than there are PAs in nephrology and hopefully PAs will wake up to the fun of kidneys! There is not a 'typical' day since the diversity is huge so I will do a thumbnail sketch for you.

It is 6:00 a.m. and my alarm is going off. Then I realize it is only my phone. Another early wakeup call from my night-time dialysis unit ☺. Eva, the nurse, had to send out a patient with shortness of breath at 4:00 a.m. but waited until a 'reasonable' hour to notify me. The ER is on it. I send an email to the doc who is covering that particular hospital, take a shower and wake my daughter for school. Since she is 12, she SLOWLY crawls out of bed, dresses and off we go. No more phone calls until she is off to school and I am in the car on the way to the dialysis unit. Then I get 3 calls in a row. I gave up a day of office hours in exchange for dialysis unit call and while that was a good decision for me, some days my phone is like an umbilical cord – especially during lab week!

I arrive at the first unit at 7:30 a.m. My patients dialyze either Monday/Wednesday/Friday or Tuesday/Thursday/Saturday. My units have 3 shifts on MWF and 2 shifts on TTS. I have 5 dialysis units for which I am responsible, with a total of 200 patients. The average treatment time is 4 hours and I need to visit with them during that time period. Each unit has a slightly different schedule (and personality) but most 1st shift patients start at 6:00 a.m., 2nd at 11:00 a.m. and 3rd shift at 3:30 p.m. We only are closed on Christmas (patients refuse to come in) and New Years Day (staff refuses to come in) since you will die without dialysis. I actually love to work holidays. My daughter and husband have a bonding day, the commute is a breeze and the unit is quiet. I always reward myself with a day off during the week when I worked a holiday. I LOVE flexibility!

I will see my half of the 200 dialysis patients any time during the week I want. The 5 doctors in my practice split the other 100 dialysis patients while covering the 4 local hospitals and the office. Since I went on the field trip with my daughter's class on Monday, I am seeing the patients on Wednesday this week. Since there are only hemoglobins to review, it is mostly a social visit. I see these patients every week for years and can get very close to them. I know their kids, grandkids, spouses and dreams. Losing a dialysis patient can be very hard. They have become a friend to us. My patients range from 18-89, **VERY** healthy to **VERY** sick, happy and cheery to severely depressed, talkative to asleep. Since most of these patients are not seen by their primary care practitioners (who are often intimidated by such 'fragile' patients), I do a lot of primary care, dermatology and orthopedics. I love the variety, but can get stumped. It is nice to know any of my 5 doctors are only a phone call away. They deal with the truly sick patients while I enjoy the outpatients. We cover a number of Trauma I hospitals and I am always shocked that we manage to keep some of these patients alive!

I head off to the office to see the patients with CKD (chronic kidney disease). Since I prefer the flexibility of the dialysis unit to the office, I only do one-half day in the office each week. I adjust blood pressure and diabetes medications, review the stages of kidney disease, manage anemia, and seem to treat a lot of primary care problems. Again, our referring primary care offices appreciate this since medication dosage adjustments for kidney excretion are second nature to me, while the general practice physicians and PAs would be spending hours looking up doses.

Earlier in the month I had agreed to give a talk sponsored by NKF (National Kidney Foundation) to a group of federal workers. Now it is 20 minutes before the talk, I am running out the door and questioning why I was so gullible. However, facing 40 people who sincerely are interested in health, kidneys, weight, blood pressure, diabetes and what they can do to stay healthy is exhilarating! Someone comes up after the talk and tells me he is going to donate a kidney to his son next month and how much he appreciated my information. I tell him how much we appreciate him and his sacrifice. I find myself going home with a smile. Now I remember why I agree to these things.

I pick up my daughter after school and head home, answering one last page as we drive. I go home and dash off an email to my group with the info on the problem patients I saw today so the on-call doctor will know what I did/saw…Each of us does this to make life for the on-call doctor so much easier! Tomorrow is Thursday, the day my group meets for breakfast. Ostensibly, it is to discuss patients but in practical terms, we discuss the patient cases, then also discuss world problems, solve the Middle East Crisis, hear about what the kids and grandkids are up to and basically enjoy 2 hours of excellent conversation. However, before I can enjoy breakfast with the guys, I need to get a very tired 12-year-old off to bed.

Neurosurgery
Association of Neurosurgical Physician Assistants
(www.anspa.org)
Submitted by Joseph A. Hlavin, PA-C

The use of physician assistants in neurosurgery was first documented in an article from 1977 authored by Dr. Sonntag. He spoke of the utilizations of physician assistants as adjuncts to the resident and fellow staff and a bridge from nursing to medicine in the care of neurosurgical patients.

We, in neurosurgery, have been fortunate to enjoy unprecedented support from the organized profession of our supervising physicians. I have been a PA in neurosurgery for over 17 years. I was lucky in that I graduated from a small PA program in Parma, OH yet had the chance to experience exceptional training in surgery. Most PA programs are primary care focused but I was able to take a surgical track in my clinical year. I was able to spend time at the Cleveland Clinic for several of my rotations, but was most impressed with the neurosurgery patient. The differences in symptom presentation even with the same illness were impressive. I was also taken in by the intricacies of the procedures in neurosurgery. Most of the work is done on delicate structures and I still enjoy the "fine-tuned" use of instrumentation in the brain and spine.

A typical day for me starts early, about 6:00 a.m. I make inpatient rounds, starting with the critical care patients in the Intensive Care Unit (ICU), and then visiting with the first surgical patient and their family. Last minute questions, checking lab work, and marking the surgical site are all part of the pre-op phase. In the OR, I get all the clinic notes in order and get films up on the viewer for the neurosurgeon to review as I get the patient draped and start the procedure. With several years of surgical experience, my supervising physician is able to place a significant amount of trust in my technical abilities. He knows I will guide the procedure along its initial track as he is preparing to "scrub in." Ultimately, we work as a team to navigate efficiently through the surgery. This style allows for the patient to get two experienced practitioners working on them, minimizing surgical and anesthetic time.

I relay information and plans initiated on rounds with the neurosurgeon in between cases and I move on to "pre-op" the next patient. We usually break at noon and then meet up again after 1:00 p.m. for outpatient clinic. I obtain a problem-focused history and physical on all of the new patients in the clinic and, if they have recent films, I present them to the neurosurgeon and we formulate a treatment plan together.

All post operative patients will see me initially and that is when instructions are provided and physical therapy started. I review any x-rays obtained and develop a plan for continued recovery. I handle all of the disability and Family Medical Leave of Absence (FMLA) forms. Routinely at the end of clinic, I return patient calls and authorize medication refills.

I finish my day at around 6:00 p.m., putting in, collectively, 60 hours a week. I take call once a week and every fourth weekend which can push that total weekly work time beyond 70 hours. I generally handle all admissions to our service and all inpatient consults. Overall, I see my role as an extension of the neurosurgeon such that he can be in two places at once.

Most general neurosurgical practices see a majority of spine related problems. Routinely, patients will have sought medical care from primary care physicians prior to being referred to us and a variety of conservative management techniques have been employed to no avail. Once we become involved, the patient is willing to contemplate some type of interventional procedure to take away pain and/or weakness. Periodically, we will have patients with intracranial pathology ranging from traumatic injuries and hemorrhages to tumors and vascular abnormalities. Usual treatment for most intracranial abnormalities is surgical and outcomes vary with diagnosis and presentation.

The challenges that face this subspecialty nationally may not be as daunting as those witnessed by other areas of the PA profession. Due to the hard work of ANSPA, the professional and political outlook for neurosurgical PAs is quite good. Inroads to policy development committees have been established and with the help of the medical industry, educational forums continue to be developed and implemented. The biggest challenge now is one that has dogged many of the constituent organizations and that is: how do we get the message of our association to the general PA public? How do we get new and seasoned PAs in neurosurgery connected? Are neurosurgical PAs satisfied with their professional lives and if not, why not? We are ready to take our organization to the next level.

Obstetrics and Gynecology
Association of Physician Assistants in Obstetrics and
Gynecology
(www.paobgyn.org)
Submitted by Sarah H. Lindahl, PA-C

There are so many different settings for PAs working in Ob/Gyn. For some the day begins by arriving in the office or clinic, reviewing charts and labs before the schedule of patient visits starts. The PA is seeing patients throughout the day and attempting to catch up with some phone calls. Some PAs are involved with precepting students. Other PAs may have their day start at a hospital, rounding on patients or preparing patients for surgery. For some the day does not end when the last patient leaves, as they carry a pager and take call for the night.

I see patients within the full spectrum of ob/gyn care including adolescent care, contraception, prenatal care, well woman visits as well as patients with abnormal pap smears and mammograms and breast masses. We evaluate gynecologic disorders and manage patients with menstrual dysfunctions, endometriosis, ovarian cysts, uterine fibroids, and osteoporosis. Some PAs work in gynecology subspecialties such as infertility, oncology and uro-gynecology.

My biggest concern for our specialty is that the high cost of malpractice is driving many physicians to leave the specialty, resulting in fewer practitioners to provide obstetric care, and creating problems with access to care for many patients in the nation. The national trend toward a higher caesarean delivery rate with fewer Vaginal Births After Caesareans (VBACs) is leading to more costly obstetric care and may lead to further patient complications.

Otolaryngology (ENT)
Society of PAs in Otorhinolaryngology/Head & Neck Surgery (www.entpa.org)
Submitted by Mel D. Brown MPAS, PA-C, President, Society of Physician Assistants in Otolaryngology and Marie Gilbert, PA-C, AAPA Medical Liaison to the American Academy of Otolaryngology - Head & Neck Surgery

I have been involved in the specialty of otolarygology in various capacities for 27 years. This started while in the USAF as a member of the Aerospace Medicine Primary Disaster Response and Recovery Team for 8 years which involved a significant component of ear, nose and throat physiology, and emergency airway management. I subsequently completed a master's program in advanced otolaryngology studies, then completed the postgraduate (then USAF now Scottsdale Mayo) Head and Neck Surgery Fellowship/Residency Program.

My days here at the University of New Mexico Health Science Center are varied and involve teaching students, residents and staff including presentations on specialty specific topics to large groups. Being a referral center and the only Level I Trauma Center in New Mexico, we receive patients of very high acuity such as advanced head and neck cancers, major trauma and last chance evaluations after the outlying private practices have no further options to offer their patients. In addition to routine diagnoses such as chronic sinusitis, tonsillitis, sleep apnea, chronic otitis media/externa, vertigo, hearing loss, swallowing and speech disorders, we also have our own diagnostic center with CT and MRI for specialties such as allergy, speech, swallowing, vestibular, sleep and hematology/oncology within the facility and are frequently involved within these subspecialty evaluations and treatments.

My days vary depending on whether I work at the hospital or the faculty clinic. Each day usually commences at 7:00 a.m., seeing upward of 20 outpatients per day plus ER consults, trauma and inpatients. I see no inpatients at the faculty clinic (2 days a week), but perform a fair number of procedures such as fiberoptic endoscopies, allergy testing, myringotomies, insertion of pressure equalization tubes, turbinate reductions, antral punctures, sinus debridements, tympanic membrane repairs, nasal fracture reductions, ear/mastoid cleanings, and scar revisions in addition to various other routine and esoteric otolaryngic conditions. Days rarely end before 6:00 p.m.

I consult with my supervising physicians on difficult cases. When there are no supervising physicians in the facility I am working in, they are never more than a phone call away. We also have a division meeting at least once a week which provides an opportunity to discuss specific issues.

The above differs significantly from Marie Gilbert, PA-C who submits:

My typical day at work begins at 7:30 a.m. and continues until 6:00 or 7:00 p.m. for 4 days per week. My patients are new consultations and patients that return for follow-up for the care they have previously received. I will see patients for all aspects of ENT medical and surgical care including preoperative patient evaluations, postoperative assessments, hospital rounds, office procedures, first call, and supervising the office medical staff. I'm also the practice administrator at my office, so I do management tasks daily.

Patients in the practice where I work have diagnoses such as otitis media, sinusitis, tonsillitis, peritonsillar abscesses, hearing loss, dysosmia, anosmia, head & neck neoplasms, thyroid disease, allergies, immunodeficiencies, balance disorders, head & neck trauma, skin lesions in the head and neck area, tinnitus (ringing in the ear), dysphagia, hoarseness, esophageal reflux, laryngopharyngeal reflux, and more.

Mel indicates that there are 3 issues which are on the forefront of the specialty which include independent practice laws, advanced specialty certification and doctoral programs for which there are no current standards and may affect credibility and further advancement. Marie adds that one of the biggest areas of struggle is trying to care for the marked increase in under-insured and uninsured patients and helping them to be able to access quality healthcare.

Pediatric Surgery
American Association of Surgical Physician Assistants (www.aaspa.com)
Submitted by Robert J. Sammartano, RPA-C, Senior Surgical PA, Pediatric Surgery; Program Director, Postgraduate Residency in Surgery for Physician Assistants; President Elect AASPA; Chief Delegate for Surgery AAPA HOD

Pediatric surgery is a very unique surgical subspecialty. Physicians in the field are required to complete several years of additional training after their surgical residency, accompanied with time spent in clinical research. I started with a distinct advantage, having had twenty years of surgical research experience working with a world-renowned pediatric surgeon prior to going to Yale to become a PA. After completing my PA program, I spent 15 months at the Montefiore Medical Center-Albert Einstein College of Medicine's Postgraduate Residency in Surgery. Immediately following that arduous task, I was hired as a PA in pediatric surgery at the same institution. For the last 6 years I have also been the program director of that surgical residency program.

In order to be effective as a PA in pediatric surgery, a delicate balance between the surgical staff, pediatric medical staff, parents, social services, family and the patient must be maintained. This often requires constant reinforcement and explanation of the surgical plan to all the aforementioned parties, sometimes several times a day as changes evolve. Once the plan is clarified and set in motion, the surgical PA is instrumental in carrying it out to completion.

As one of only a handful of pediatric surgical PAs in the country, my responsibilities include participation in daily morning and afternoon patient rounds (where I formulate a treatment plan to present to my supervising physicians or assure the one previously agreed to by my surgical attendings is being correctly implemented); first-assisting during surgery for various types of cases (open and laparoscopic); performing bedside procedures in the outpatient office, in-patient treatment areas and ambulatory settings; evaluating patients in the emergency department; acting as a surgical consult on the in-patient floors (NICU, PCCU, SICU, hematology-oncology, nephrology, transplant, neurology and neurosurgery) and for the outpatient pediatric offices adjacent to our institution. I participate in all aspects of the outpatient surgical care, preoperatively and postoperatively. Working in a large academic medical center, I assist the surgical residents on our service with the presentation of interesting cases at Pediatric Surgery Grand Rounds and often present cases on my own. I also serve as an instructor for the physician residents and the PA surgical residents, teaching them to recognize pediatric surgical disease, its embryologic origin, the most recent projected outcomes described in the literature, and the long-term impact on the patient's life. I extend my role as an educator by lecturing on pediatric surgery locally to PA programs in my area, statewide through the New York State Society of Physician Assistants (NYSSPA), and nationally through the American Association of Surgical Physician Assistants (AASPA) and AAPA.

Rounding out my pediatric surgical PA role, I participate on an equal level with my physician colleagues as a member of the Umbrella Committee of the Department of Surgery for Quality Issues and the overall policy-making body of the institution, the Division Council. It is exceptionally important that PAs have a voice in the policing of their practice and the direction their institution takes in caring for patients, structuring services, managing personnel and setting financial goals.

Plastic Surgery
Association of Plastic Surgery Physician Assistants
(www.apspa.net)
Submitted by Chrysa Charno, RPA-C, MBA; Vega Aesthetic & Reconstructive Surgery- Pittsford, NY; Secretary of the Association of Plastic Surgery Physician Assistants; Lifetime Health Afterhours- Rochester, NY

The field of plastic surgery is very unique in that you are working on all parts of the human body to satisfy the needs of both the reconstructive and cosmetic patient. When I first became a PA I worked in the field of orthopedics. Being a rookie is never easy, but the repetitive nature of the field made it easy to pick up the skills needed for working in the operating room, managing acute fractures and taking care of outpatient sports medicine patients. But after a few months of this, I reconsidered and I thought medicine would be a better niche. I took a job with a local urgent care center, working closely with the physician to manage a walk-in center. After a year of training alongside my supervising physician, I was left alone for my shifts to manage 40-50 patients per day with acute care needs (sore throats, fractures, headaches, injuries). Even though I enjoyed full-time acute care, there was still a void in my life and I finally figured out that it was the operating room - the one major reason why I wanted to be a PA in the first place.

Hearing that there was an unadvertised position with a plastic surgeon at the local university, I found his contact information and sent my resume along with a personalized letter. One meeting led to another and I found myself with a position working alongside one of the highest volume microsurgeons in the Northeast. We first worked together at the local teaching university, utilizing physician residents for rounding and emergency patient care. After three years in practice, we decided to move into a private practice and now have complete autonomy. The beauty of the PA practice is the flexibility that our training allows. Not only do I have a full-time job in a private plastic surgery practice, but I also spend time in the urgent care setting after hours on a per-diem basis which allows me to take care of children and medical conditions that I wouldn't encounter every day in surgery.

I usually get up at 5:00 a.m. which allows me enough time to get to the hospital and round on our patients before we start in the operating room at 7:30 a.m. Typically when I arrive, I stop by the pre-anesthesia area and greet our first patient, making sure that all of the appropriate testing has been completed. We then go over the details of the procedure, post-operative care, medications and finally the surgical consent form. The surgeon that I work with specializes in microsurgery, which allows us the ability to take tissue from one part of the body, completely detach it, bring the tissue to the area of deficit and sew together the artery and vein in that area for blood supply. We do this frequently for breast cancer patients who undergo mastectomies and require reconstruction. What a rewarding service to provide- a breast cancer patient gets a tummy tuck AND a new reconstructed breast that feels like her own! On this particular day we have two major reconstructive cases, a breast and a mandible! Our second patient's information is also reviewed to reveal a 54-year-old male with squamous cell cancer of the floor of the mouth extending into the jaw. For this case we work in conjunction with a head and neck surgeon who removes the jaw and then we use a piece of the fibula (with muscle, fat and skin) to make a new one!

Once the first patient is ready and taken into the operating room, I prepare to scrub with my surgeon, making sure to prepare and drape the patient's body in a way that we both can work together. The next five hours are busy. The general surgeon removes the breast while we harvest tissue from the abdomen, preparing the single artery and vein we will be using for the flap to survive on the chest wall. Once the chest wall is prepared, we detach the flap from the abdomen and bring it to the chest wall. Because we no longer have physician residents, I assist my surgeon with the actual sewing of the vessels. Once we have good blood supply, I am left to close the abdominal wall fascia, fat and skin while he molds the new tissue into a breast mound. These patients spend a few days in the hospital so that our new tissue can be monitored. After surgery, I take care of the admission orders and get ready to scrub into our second case.

By now the head and neck surgeon has been working for 3 hours. We immediately scrub in together and approach the right lower leg. My job is critical here as I am the one responsible for exposing and handling the vessels so that my surgeon can prepare them for reconstruction. Once a large piece of fibula, muscle, fat and skin is separated and removed from the patient, we use a saw so that the angles of the mandible can be measured and reconstructed on this new piece of bone. Again we perform the same microsurgical technique and, when complete, the patient hardly looks like he had his jaw completely removed and reconstructed with a piece of his leg.

By now its 5:00 p.m. and lunch sounds good, but its time for dinner. Together as a team, my surgeon and I round on our first operative patient and she looks great. I take care of a few patient phone calls that came across my pager, grab some food from Subway® at the hospital and jump into my car to Afterhours. My shift tonight is from 6:00 p.m. to 10:00 p.m. and I will see things like sore throats, ear infections and colds. The patient population is all ages and because I work in surgery I frequently am the one to get all of the procedures like suturing, removing soft tissue foreign bodies or draining abscesses.

By the time I get home and in bed, its 10:30 p.m. I take all of the call for our private practice Monday through Friday nights so my pager sits on my nightstand. Tomorrow we have a clinic in the morning to take care of postoperative patients and perform cosmetic injectables including Botox®, Juvéderm®, Radiesse® and Restylane®. This is followed by time at an outpatient surgery center to consult with patients about breast augmentation, breast reduction and then liposuction.

One of the biggest challenges that we face in the field of plastic surgery is the utilization and scope of practice of PAs. We are frequently faced with issues from different states that don't allow PAs to perform certain procedures like injecting fillers or using lasers. In some areas of the country, doctors in other specialties are performing procedures generally considered to be the scope of practice of the plastic surgeon. However, despite some of the challenges of practice restrictions in some states, PAs practicing in this specialty are generally extremely happy. Their practice is filled with variety as they frequently follow the patient from the first encounter, through their surgery and into their recovery. I am a perfect example of how flexible a PA can be. In my mind there is no better combination than surgery AND medicine.

Psychiatry
Association of Psychiatric Physician Assistants
(www.psychpa.com)
Submitted by Don St. John, PA-C

I work in an outpatient setting seeing adult patients with psychiatric diseases. I have one-half hour appointments because of the academic setting that I am in. I perform initial consultations and medication checks. I utilize both written and oral assessment tools and can diagnose and discuss treatment options with the patient and family. Because I have a degree in clinical psychology, I also do psychotherapy. Most PAs in psychiatry do not perform psychotherapy, but there are a few that do because of supplemental training. In the last survey done of the membership of PAs in Psychiatry, we found that 40% of PAs in psychiatry have a degree in another mental health related field. That survey was done a few years ago and I think that percentage may have decreased considerably.

Because of the setting I am in, I see a lot of disorders that are treatment resistant. So, I get patients that have already been on several different medication regimens and they get referred to our center because their disorders are difficult to treat. That is somewhat unique to my practice. I see a lot of patients with personality disorders, severe depression, attention deficit and hyperactivity disorder, and post-traumatic stress disorder. Many other PAs in psychiatry work in inpatient settings, nursing homes and at the Veterans Administration. In some psychiatric settings, the supervising physician is a non-mental health specialist such as an internist.

Reimbursement is our biggest issue nationally. We still receive many denials of payment from insurance companies. Psychiatric benefits have been "carved out", so mental health services are paid through different carriers than medical services. It still seems that even large, well-established payers do not know enough about our profession. We are often on the phone educating them regarding what a PA is, to help them understand that we can bill for the same services as a physician. I think this field is growing rapidly for PAs especially in response to the shortage of psychiatrists in many demographic areas. We work closely with the psychiatric physician organizations to promote the PA profession.

Rheumatology
Society of Physician Assistants in Rheumatology
(www. rheumpas.org)
Submitted by Susan Richmond, M.S. PA-C

I am fortunate to work in a private rheumatology practice, which is involved in the diagnosis, treatment, and monitoring of autoimmune diseases such as rheumatoid arthritis, lupus, polymyalgia rheumatica, systemic sclerosis and other conditions. Rheumatology also involves treatment of other types of arthritis and musculoskeletal problems, for example osteoarthritis, gout, tendinopathy, and carpal tunnel syndrome. Fibromyalgia is a growing area of study that is also treated by rheumatology PAs. I find the field to be rewarding in that it frequently deals with diagnostic puzzles, as rheumatic diseases can be obscure but careful, thoughtful investigation can lead to an accurate diagnosis and treatment.

During a typical day in clinical practice, I begin seeing scheduled patients, which may include a combination of new patients or follow-up appointments. These visits focus on evaluation for rheumatic disease and initiation of appropriate treatment plans in new patients. For established patients, I am responsible for assessing response to treatment, addressing any new problems including medication side effects, and altering therapies as appropriate. Laboratory and other testing is also reviewed or ordered, depending upon the patient's response to treatment and findings on clinical examination. Interspersed with patient visits, I also review messages from patients who have contacted the office with questions, and return calls or place orders depending on the problem presented.

In my rheumatology office, we have the advantage of utilizing musculoskeletal ultrasound. This technique is used to assist in diagnosing inflammatory arthropathies, as well as for diagnosis and treatment of other musculoskeletal disorders.

Using musculoskeletal ultrasound, I'm able to identify problems such as rotator cuff tears, calcific tendinitis, crystals, and synovial thickening. Synovial thickening is seen in rheumatoid arthritis or in other conditions such as Lyme disease, and ultrasound findings can assist in formulation of treatment plans or further testing. I use ultrasound for guidance of injections, aspiration of effusions, and to assist in the treatment of localized arthritic and other musculoskeletal conditions.

Since I am working in a solo practice, I may consult my supervising physician to review a new plan of care, address concerns regarding a change of condition, or update the physician regarding alterations of an existing plan of care in certain patients. We may collaborate to work out a complicated treatment, or to review unusual cases, which are often found in the field of rheumatology.

In addition to regular medical duties, I've been fortunate to have the opportunity to provide rheumatology lectures to physician assistant students. As a PA in rheumatology, you can join your colleagues as a member of the Society for Physician Assistants in Rheumatology (SPAR), which is working to enhance this specialty for physician assistants, as well as help to educate other physician assistants about the specialty.

While there are a small number of physician assistants in rheumatology, this specialty offers a growing opportunity for employment of new or established physician assistants. It is very satisfying, as emerging treatments have led to restore comfort and function in many patients, who are then able to return to everyday life activities. It is a field that will challenge you to provide care to patients with complex medical conditions, and position you on the front line of emerging therapies and technology for treatment of arthritis, autoimmune disease, and other musculoskeletal problems.

Urology
Urologic Association of Physician Assistants
(www.uapanet.org)
Submitted by Wanda C. Hancock, MHSA, PA-C

My typical day is busy with a mixture of patients in consults and follow-up. Much of my day is spent with patients suffering from lower urinary tract disorders such as benign prostatic hypertrophy (BPH), interstitial cystitis, neurogenic bladder, and overactive bladder. Urinary retention and chronic cystitis are prevalent in our practice. I also see a number of patients with erectile dysfunction issues such as Peyronie's disease, priapism, and the inability to get erections. I see patients to confirm a diagnosis and offer conservative management of testicular masses that include hydroceles, varicoceles, and spermatoceles. I am involved with the follow up care of patients after surgery for renal, testicular, prostate, and bladder cancers. We are doing more treatment of recurrent prostate cancer with hormonal manipulation. We manage the post operative treatment of bladder cancers. In our practice, the PAs do not perform cystoscopies and prostate biopsies; however, in other practices across the nation PAs will do these procedures on a regular basis. Other procedures in our clinic include penile biopsies, microwave therapy for BPH, and performing urodynamic diagnostic studies.

Many PAs in urology work in the operating room (OR) as a first assist and spend at least 2 days a week in the OR. Some PAs are hospital-based and see patients for an initial consultation, then round on patients daily throughout their inpatient stay. PAs may be called to consult on urgent care patients as well. While the PAs in our practice do not see pediatric patients, there are a number that do and these PAs primarily treat voiding dysfunction. Some PAs have been trained and routinely perform vasectomies, hydrocelectomies and circumcisions.

Interaction with my supervising physician is primarily for consultation if there are questions concerning management or a particular diagnosis. If the patient is a surgical candidate, the surgeon will meet with the patient to assure that there are no questions concerning the proposed surgery and to establish a relationship with the patient. After the surgery, the patient will meet with the surgeon for the first post operative visit. Once the patient is stable, he/she will follow up with one of the PAs in our office.

There are fewer urologists than are needed at this time but this will likely change. There has been a paucity of urologists over the past 10 years and along with that an increase in the number of PAs entering the field. Although my opinion has not been validated with a study, it seems that most PAs who select urology are very happy and tend to stay in the field for a number of years.

Are there even more?

Many physicians in other fields of medicine are finding that PAs are a beneficial addition to their practice. These growing fields are not recognized as an AAPA Specialty Organization, but have been gaining in popularity in recent years and worth including here.

Hospital Administration
Submitted by Jim Delaney, PA-C

After many years of clinical practice, I decided to take an administrative position for the surgical services which includes orthopedics, podiatry, plastic surgery, vascular surgery and general surgery. I provide administrative oversight of these departments for the ambulatory (outpatient) setting as well as the surgical scheduling of providers, cases and patients.

I usually arrive at work at around 6:00-6:30 a.m. to make sure that we are completely staffed in the clinics and at the multiple operating room locations to minimize surgery cancellations. I also need to verify that staff is covering all of the inpatient services at two hospitals. I have direct responsibility for the providers including 31 physicians, 8 podiatrists, 31 PAs and 3 NPs in addition to over one hundred support staff of medical assistants, registered nurses and clerical staff. I am responsible for providing quality and safety support for the department and regulatory compliance oversight for the clinic and staff. I work Monday through Friday and usually do not get out until 5:30-6:00 p.m. after addressing these multiple issues.

Throughout the day I will have multiple meetings with the operating room director, hospital leadership and medical group leadership. I also meet with the appointment staff leadership for weekly updates on new and return patient access times for all services. In addition, I sit on a number of hospital committees, providing direction for the hospital in general. I provide support to the regional offices for PA practice oversight to all of our Southern California locations and assist with issues surrounding NP/PA privileging and credentialing. This is scheduled around my daily problem-solving for access to care issues, operating room support, emergency case scheduling, evening call and general administrative support to the outlying clinics.

I continue to provide direct patient care to orthopedic patients for one full day per week in order to maintain my clinical skills.

The difficulty that I run into as a PA in hospital administration is that I am in a role traditionally held by a registered nurse. I believe I have brought a different set of eyes to the role because of my provider background. The organization leadership has recognized the advantages that my additional knowledge brings in helping solve some challenging situations. My experience in my profession's leadership and my interest in privileging/credentialing has allowed for the expansion of scope of practice and advancement of PA roles both on an ambulatory level as well as on the hospital level.

Infectious Diseases
Submitted by Ryann Morrison, MS, PA-C, Founder of AAPA special interest group Physician Assistants in Infectious Diseases

In the 3 years that I have been a practicing PA in infectious diseases I have found it to be a rewarding and challenging experience. I started the special interest group through AAPA in order to reach out and meet other PAs practicing in the specialty, and I was happily surprised to come into contact with a variety of infectious disease practices around the US. I found that some of the other PAs in infectious diseases have a day much different than my own, seeing patients in the outpatient setting, including HIV clinics.

My day is spent rounding on hospital inpatients in a tertiary care 1,000 bed facility. In a specialty like infectious disease we are asked to see a wide range of patients and disease processes. It's not like other specialties that deal primarily with one specific organ system or disorder - as infectious disease PAs we see it all. We are consulted for cellulitis, osteomyelitis, pneumonia, empyema, blood stream infections, meningitis, endocarditis, urinary tract infections, intra-abdominal abscesses and infections, septic arthritis, prosthetic joint infections, HIV, Clostridium difficile diarrhea, fever of unknown origin, fever in the neutropenic patients and wound infections, just to list a few. Every part of the body has the ability to get infected, and when it does, they call on the infectious disease specialists to treat.

When I round in the hospital, I typically see 12-15 patients a day in follow-up with an additional 1-2 consults. The follow-up inpatients take up the entire morning from 8:00 a.m. until noon. After a break for lunch, I typically re-round with my attending physician and break away to do the late day consults before signing out to the physician and heading home around 5:00 p.m. It's common in our practice to see both follow-up and consult patients with the physician. The physicians have been trained with an additional 2 years of fellowship beyond their residency to practice specifically with infectious diseases, and as my learning catches up to the years of fellowship training, they start to utilize us similar to fellows in infectious disease, not "mid-level providers". We are able to triage patients, make appropriate medical decisions, and streamline the physician's day so that it may be spent on more difficult cases, or in the outpatient office seeing hospital follow ups or travelers heading to a far away land, since my office has multiple physicians certified in travel medicine.

Some of the other events in which I participate involve furthering our education and learning from other health care providers. Every other Wednesday we go to the microbiology lab to share information. The PAs write case reports and present them to the lab staff. They in turn show us the relevant microbiology associated with the case, and give a mini-lecture to teach us about a variety of microbes. In addition, I attend weekly hospital medicine grand rounds and participate in our practices' journal club. Three to four people, both physicians and PAs, present case reports and new journal articles, we make comments and sometimes arguments based on the literature. We try to follow case and evidence based learning, medicine and practices. It is one of the ways we try to stay current with all the changes in infectious diseases. Alone it would be impossible to sort through all the literature monthly and this way each of us takes our share and presents it to the group.

Some of the issues and challenges that face PA's in infectious diseases are not that unique to the specialty. The question of the benefit of additional specialty training in post graduate programs and doctorate programs is controversial. It isn't easy to go directly from graduation into a specialty practice and feel like you know what you're doing. The education received in a PA program has suited the profession thus far since we have a vast knowledge of general medicine, but have the capability to focus our talents in one specialty. The flexibility truly makes our usefulness undeniable. Even though PA's are underutilized in this field, those of us practicing in infectious disease realize that our presence is greatly appreciated and needed. We hope that other physicians and PAs are open to the idea of increasing the numbers of physician assistants in infectious disease.

Interventional Radiology
Submitted by Linda Morrison PA-C

To me, the most enjoyable aspect of being an interventional radiology (IR) PA is the wide variety of patient care opportunities that come with the specialty. Most IR PAs are hospital based, and so we must obtain hospital privileges in order to see in-patients and perform procedures. Some IR PAs (myself included) work in large radiology practices that also have free-standing out-patient facilities where IR patients can be seen and treated outside of a hospital setting.

In interventional radiology, we can access almost any part of the body using real-time image guidance. Our procedures may be performed using fluoroscopy, CT, or ultrasound guidance. Using our "minimally invasive techniques" we can treat and cure diseases which otherwise could only be treated or cured with surgery. Interventional radiologists invented the balloon angioplasty and stenting procedures, and in our specialty we can open blocked blood vessels just about anywhere in the body. We can treat cancerous tumors using radiofrequency ablation and chembolization. We place drainage tubes to cure abscesses, chest tubes to drain pleural effusions or expand collapsed lungs, and perform image-guided biopsies of just about any body part. We treat dialysis patients by opening blocked AV grafts and fistulas. We can insert any type of central venous catheter, including chest and arm ports, tunneled dialysis catheters, and multi-lumen central lines. Interventional radiologists can even stop life-threatening brain bleeding without neurosurgery, and can mend spinal fractures almost instantaneously by injecting specially-formulated bone cement into the fractured vertebrae. There is seemingly no end to the list of maladies than can be treated or cured in our specialty.

As an IR PA, my day would include seeing clinic patients pre or post-procedure, performing procedures on my own, and rounding on hospital patients. An IR PA's scope of practice varies all over the country, and would depend on what is customary in the particular state or hospital system involved. Many IR PAs are taught a large number of procedures by their supervising physicians, who eventually become comfortable with the PA's competence to perform that procedure independently. Supervising physicians are available to consult on difficult or unusual cases or procedures. This specialty is yet another wonderful example of the physician – physician assistant team practice concept.

As I see it, the biggest struggles facing my specialty are the restrictive fluoroscopy laws which are present in many states. Using fluoroscopy is crucial in the performance of a large number of IR procedures, so many of which are well within the scope of practice of a PA. By restricting the use of fluoroscopy to physicians only, delays in patient care or the number of patients treated on any given day are significantly altered. Fluoroscopy is a mode of imaging that is extremely safe in the hands of a trained operator, and PAs must be given the opportunity to demonstrate their competency in this medium. Changing such restrictive laws would significantly improve access to quality patient care.

Outside of the United States

The PA profession is growing and becoming a model for other countries as well. There are PAs now at least on a trial basis in England, Australia, and Canada where there is socialized medicine. We were lucky to get a submission to give you a feel for working as a PA across the border!

The Canadian Neurosurgical Physician Assistant
Submitted by Ian W. Jones, MPAS, PA-C / CA cert
Section of Neurosurgery, Winnipeg Regional Health Authority

In Canada, for years the only physician assistants to be found were in the Canadian Forces. These Canadians came from the ranks to take additional training to qualify as a PA, but could not practice in the civilian world. Their contributions on ships, field operations, and in base clinic are invaluable. With hard work and much patience the governments in the provinces, first Manitoba then Ontario, realized that the knowledge base and skills of the PA could improve patient care and physician efficiency.

I am a Canadian who discovered the physician assistant profession during a career search when an injury forced me to switch jobs from a life as a firefighter-paramedic. The ability to practice medicine, switching environments and specialties, and building a career with responsibility, challenges, and opportunity was very appealing. With PA training from the University of Washington's MEDEX program and later earning a master's degree, I practiced in family and emergency medicine for ten years in America before a chance to come home arose. In the city of Winnipeg, Manitoba, physician assistants were needed to help with neurosurgical patients. The role of a physician assistant, called a clinical assistant in Manitoba, is of peri-operative support. The PA rotates from the outpatient clinic where they perform history and physical examinations, then move to daytime ward duty caring for the in-patients, and then in-hospital night call. This rotation permits the PA to work with the attending neurosurgeons evaluating patients, taking in-hospital consults, learning, and improving the collaborative relationship. The neurosurgical clinic has the PA examining new patients and performing post-operative follow ups, ordering additional studies, if indicated, and coordinating admissions while the attending fields calls, completes documentation on other patients, or evaluates another patient, improving overall productivity. The PA gathers the essential background information from which to build the patients care. On the ward, rounds are completed with the residents, who can then leave for educational sessions or the operating room, allowing the PA to manage medical care, adjust orders, perform tasks, or generally perform the traditional duties of a house medical officer, and provide the neurosurgery consulting services. On my service I work *with* my residents but work *for* the attending neurosurgeons. The first line of support for me is the service's residents; however, the attending and supervising physician is always available for support and case review.

I work in a large academic, trauma, and specialty service hospital. This means I am connected to a university medical school, and we receive patients from a region that covers the Arctic, Western Ontario, and Manitoba - a land mass bigger than Texas and several other states combined. My service cares for paediatric and adult patients and provides a wide range of neurological surgical care. Winnipeg's neurosurgeons treat trauma and diseases of the spine and brain, coil and clip cerebral aneurysms, deal with tumours, and address facial nerve issues such as trigeminal neuralgia and facial spasm. The list is extensive and it requires the physician assistant who works in neurosurgery to spend a lot of time learning and improving their knowledge. Personally it is hard to imagine an occupation with such a demand, personal challenge, and eventual personal reward could be found.

When duties and schedules permit I assist in the operating room. However, the priority is ensuring that the patient is cared for before and after surgery, in either the intensive care or surgical ward. My assistance in surgery would include positioning the patient, opening and closing the surgical incision, handling the drill or suction, or as directed by the surgeon. Where I work, neurosurgery residents, who train for 6 years, are normally available for the operating room tasks. With additional service training and experience the responsibilities of the Winnipeg neurosurgical physician assistants has increased. It now includes the placement of extra-ventricular drains, (a tube into the brain's ventricles to drain excessive cerebral spinal fluid) and providing the surgical holes which are called twist drills or bore holes for draining of subdural haematomas (blood compressing the brain). We also place monitors to measure intra-cerebral pressure, do diagnostic and therapeutic lumbar punctures, and other procedures as required.

Is it any different working in Canada compared with the USA? In Canada, our office staff does not worry about insurance status, or ability to pay for services since there is universality of care and a single payer system. There may be the occasional delay getting some elective services, however the equipment and qualifications of the staff in my hospital are first class. Having worked in the US and Canada, I feel the differences in care across borders are hard to find, but may be easier seen if you look at a business model or a service model. The joy in being a PA is that our knowledge and experiences continues to expand with each day spent providing patient care.

Is there a limit?

There really is no limit to the setting or specialty in which a physician assistant can work. If there is a physician in practice who wants to hire a PA, then it can be done. If you are considering going into a specialty and do not find a specialty organization, check with the AAPA to see if there is a special interest group. Often you can find other PAs to network with and find answers to your questions.

The Dreaded Regulatory Stuff

Malpractice

When we practice medicine, we are liable for everything that we do. We are ultimately responsible for the actions that we take, but our supervising physician is as well. Don't start seeing patients without malpractice insurance. Even if you did nothing wrong, a lawsuit against you can be very costly. Your employer may offer this as a benefit. PAs can usually be placed as a rider on a physician's malpractice insurance. If your employer does not offer this to you as a benefit, inquire about the cost of being included with the physician and you can pay the premiums directly. There are national malpractice insurance groups that will sell a physician assistant malpractice insurance directly. This is imperative if you are self employed or if you work as an independent contractor. Some PAs will also buy additional insurance even if they are covered through their employer. This may be advisable in certain specialties (i.e. surgery or ob/gyn) but in general the rider with your employer will be sufficient.

State Laws

Familiarize yourself with the laws in your state. Your licensing agency should be able to assist you in getting information about the laws that govern your practice. You are responsible for knowing the laws that regulate your profession. READ THEM and make sure you understand them. By accepting a license to practice medicine, you are acknowledging that you understand what that license allows you to do. Although most PAs may perform the duties that are delegated to them by their supervising physician, you cannot rely on that physician to know all the limitations to your scope of practice.

If you have been practicing in one state and want to practice in another, you will need to apply for a license or registration in the new state. Prepare for this. It may take many months to process a new license depending on the state. Do not assume that you know the laws because you have been practicing for years. Make sure you find out how PAs are regulated in the new state. If you are not practicing in compliance with the state laws, you may be putting your license in jeopardy. For instance, as of this writing, in Arizona, the PA and supervising physician must meet weekly according to state law. In the District of Columbia, the physician must countersign all outpatient medical orders and progress notes within 10 days. In Indiana, the PA must prove that he has worked for a full year and completed specific pharmacology classes in order to prescribe medications. In Virginia, the physician must see the patient during a follow-up visit if the condition has not improved and the physician must see the patient with continuing illness at least every fourth visit. These laws are very specific to the state, and it is your responsibility to know the law and follow every aspect of it when you are in that state. I have gathered a listing of all the state medical and/or physician assistant boards that govern physician assistant practice and that is listed in the appendix of this book.

DEA

If you are writing prescriptions for controlled substances in your practice, you will need to register to do so through the Drug Enforcement Administration (DEA). You can find specific information at www.deadiversion.usdoj.gov. Controlled substances in schedule II through IV are prescription drugs that are considered to have potential for abuse and/or can cause physical or psychological addiction[1].

Billing for Services

Insurance fraud can cost you your license and can get you jail time. It isn't good no matter how you look at it. "I would never do that" you're thinking. Oh, but you might. And, you might do it without even realizing it! Many offices allow staff or billing professionals to "help" you with your coding and billing. Make sure you understand what you are billing for and the coverage rules of the particular payer. With the advent of electronic medical records, many physicians and PAs are now entering in their own procedure (Current Procedural Terminology or CPT) codes and diagnostic (ICD-9) codes as they chart. This makes it a lot safer as long as no one is changing anything down the line. If a bill goes to an insurance company with your name on it, for a service you provided, you are the person with whom the

---

1   http://www.usdoj.gov/dea/pubs/csa/812.htm

insurance company representative will want to talk. Much like you may delegate the task of calling a prescription in to a pharmacy – if someone on your staff calls in the wrong directions for that prescription, you are ultimately responsible because it was your prescription. If billing personnel are "upcoding" or charging higher levels of services than what you are providing without your knowledge, this is considered insurance fraud. If this is happening when they bill Medicare, now you are messing with the feds and whoever engaged in the fraudulent behavior is at serious risk of receiving steep fines as well as disciplinary action. If you did not engage in fraudulent behavior and did not try to cover up that behavior, then you will likely not be charged. However, because your name is on the claim, the auditors will probably place you at the center of an investigation.

Do random audits of your own charts to make sure what you think you are billing is actually what is being billed. Some offices have an internal audit process set up amongst the physicians and other providers and you should be involved so you know the process. Your office may even hire an outside company to do an audit for you which will allow you to review your charts and billing to make sure the coding matches. Again, stay involved with these processes if possible and ask for feedback on your charts specifically.

PAs bill for their services either under the supervising physician or under their own names with reimbursement going to the PA's employer. It is important that your billing staff understand how to bill for services delivered by PAs to maximize your reimbursement and minimize rejected claims. This is not an easy task and there are reasons why there are medical billing companies out there that claim to be able to get your bills paid. Remember our friend the family physician from Chapter Three? His system works – just have patients pay up front and try to get reimbursed from their insurance companies. The only problem is that most patients aren't going to do that anymore. They will gripe about paying their $10 co-pay to see you at times! So, your supervising physician will be faced with having to contract with and bill the insurance companies for your services. Hopefully you have a billing staff or service that knows their stuff. But, you should be aware of the process. All PAs should have their own National

Provider Identifier (NPI) Number which you can apply for on-line at https://nppes.cms.hhs.gov/NPPES/Welcome.do or by calling 1-800-465-3203. The Centers for Medicare & Medicaid Services (CMS) has developed the National Plan and Provider Enumeration System (NPPES) to assign these unique identifiers. PAs must initially apply for this number and must notify them every time you start working with another physician or group that bills Medicare.

Other insurance companies must use this identification number as well. Some insurance companies require that you use an identifier on your billing that indicates that a PA saw the patient. Except in specific situations called "incident to" billing, Medicare will reimburse the physician 85% of the physician rate when a PA sees the patient. Most insurance companies will reimburse at the physician's contracted rate regardless of who provided the services as long as that provider was working within his scope of practice. Medicaid has a separate payment system in place that varies from state to state so it is important to look into whether you need to apply to be a provider within your state's Medicaid system. Managed care plans or Independent Practice Associations (IPAs) that contract with managed care plans may require that you be credentialed through that organization. With HMO contracts, each physician can be responsible for a designated number of lives and that number is often increased if the physician employs a PA. Familiarize yourself with specific billing practices especially if you work in a diverse clinic that bills multiple insurance companies, and pay special attention if you deliver services to state or federal workers' compensation patients or the veteran's administration to make sure you are meeting current guidelines.

PAs are not often listed as Primary Care Providers (PCP) in managed care organizations. So, if my neighbor has HMO (health maintenance organization) insurance and she is looking for a PCP, she can go on-line or look in the book that she got with her new insurance card. The physicians are listed by specialty and she can pick a pediatrician or family practice physician for her kids and a family practice physician or internal medicine physician for herself. She won't know at that point that a PA is working at her PCP's office. She may enjoy the fact that the PA is there because she will be able to get in sooner to be seen and will have great satisfaction with that PA. But, the physician is still considered her PCP. Maybe she even calls and requests to see the PA for a particular problem because she has built a trusting relationship with him. There is really no better compliment in my professional day when I find out that the patient requested to see me because they knew they only could talk with me about a particular problem! That is fine, but the physician is still the PCP. That is what the team practice approach is all about. I can provide care and develop relationships with patients, and I can trust that my supervising physician is there in case I need a consult or if a situation is too complex for me.

Many nurse practitioner organizations are working hard with insurance companies to try to become PCPs. Often they want to be listed in those provider manuals. They want my neighbor to be able to choose between a physician and a nurse practitioner to be their PCP. Although it may be nice at some point to be listed in a provider manual so that a patient is able to find a particular PA that has changed to a new practice, we do not take the place of the physician as the leader of the team.

Michael Powe is the Vice President of Health Systems and Reimbursement Policy at the AAPA and is an invaluable resource. He provides the following insight regarding reimbursement:

> *Obtaining fair and appropriate reimbursement for medical and surgical services is a dynamic, and occasionally frustrating, experience. PAs, physicians and other health care professionals all face challenges with third party payment.*

> *But before we talk about the money or the business of medicine we must be clear about what PAs bring to the table. The quality of care delivered by PAs remains the most important part of their contribution to the health care system. Equally important is the high level of patient satisfaction in dealing with PAs that often leads to a better understanding of their medical condition and adherence to treatment plans. And we can't forget about how PAs increase physician quality of life by reducing patient*

loads, sharing call at times, and providing them with additional time off.

In addition to these important attributes, PAs also generate additional dollars for the practice. And no practice can afford not to maximize the legitimate reimbursement to which PAs are entitled. Understanding the fact that each payer is different and can have its own requirements for covering services provided by PAs makes it imperative that PAs, physicians, and the billing personnel know the rules.

Be aware that there are many important services that PAs deliver that never show up in the reimbursement column. A third party payer may want the PA's services billed under the physician, and that is not a problem. It just means that at the end of the month or at year's end, it must be understood that some portion of the PA's reimbursement was credited to the supervising physician. Likewise, certain services that PAs perform, such as pre- and post-operative services, are typically not separately billable, but the services must be provided. If the PA delivers these non-billable services, the physician is freed up to deliver other billable services. The value of a PA goes beyond just what is billable. The PA's value and productivity is his or her total contribution to the practice and to assuring that patients receive the highest quality care.

The bottom line on billing is that we all need to get paid! Physician reimbursement is decreasing – they are contracting at lower rates to provide more services. You are going to stay employed as a PA in a practice because the patients and physicians like you and because you are good at what you do. But, you also need to bring in some money. So, make sure you are billing accurately and that you are billing for all the services you can bill for legally. If you are in a specialized practice or in an unusual setting, contact the AAPA and ask someone on the reimbursement staff to talk with you and your office about maximizing your billing and doing it correctly. There is not a better resource that completely understands billing for services provided by PAs. The AAPA also has issue briefs on many specific specialty settings including surgery settings, nursing homes, house calls, and rural healthcare settings[2]. You may need to reference these resources if you or your billing staff is working with an insurance company about your billing practices. They also publish and update a guide for reimbursement called *Physician Assistant Third-Party Coverage*, a comprehensive summary of coverage and billing information for services provided by physician assistants. You can order your copy from the on-line AAPA Store[3]. There are very cost-effective ways to utilize a PA, but you need to be billing properly for the services that you provide.

Maintaining Certification

In chapter two we talked about initial certification. You really don't have a choice about that. You cannot get your initial license to practice in any state without first graduating from an accredited program AND passing the national certifying exam. Now you have graduated from a PA program and passed the boards, and then you start practicing and call yourself a PA-C. Do you have to maintain your certification? Not necessarily, but most PAs do. In order to continue to be certified, you must complete 100 hours of continuing medical education (CME) every two years. This can include going to medical conferences that are accredited by physician or physician assistant organizations including AAPA[4], AMA[5], ACCME[6], AOACCME[7], or AAFP[8].

Don't worry, you won't have to look far to find these courses. Most state PA organizations hold at least an annual conference. The AAPA does as well. Your employer may require or request that you attend a specific conference. You will get magazines and flyers in the mail and email announcements for conferences. Some are outstanding and some are not, some are free and others are very expensive. As long as they indicate that they offer

---

2   http://www.aapa.org/gandp/3rdparty.html#mpchart

3   http://www.aapa.org/aapastore/index.html

4   http://www.aapa.org

5   http://www.ama-assn.org

6   http://www.accme.org

7   http://www.do-online.org

8   http://www.aafp.org

accredited CME, they will help you meet the requirement. You can also get CME from journals including the Journal of the American Academy of Physician Assistants (JAAPA). If you are a member of the AAPA, this is a member benefit (see Chapter 5 for more on this). You can read specific articles within the journal and answer questions on-line to get CME. Other journals offer similar CME programs that you can do on-line or by mail, sometimes for free and sometimes for a nominal fee. There are more and more on-line programs, podcasts and virtual lectures that offer CME and most of these will qualify, again as long as they are accredited.

Fifty of your CME hours will need to be pre-approved, accredited hours. The other 50 hours can still be from pre-approved, accredited programs, but can also include activities that are not accredited including reading journals, acting as a preceptor and other self-guided activities. It is best to enter these hours and classes on-line through the NCCPA as you do them rather than wait until close to the deadline. The on-line program is easy to navigate and will keep track of what you have entered as you go along. There is a fee every 2 years to enter and log your CME with the NCCPA.

The second requirement to maintain your certification is a recertification board exam every six years. Oh, the dreaded "recert"! You will hear your physician colleagues talk about this as well since most will need to take board recertification exams to maintain their specialty board certification. It seems a little silly really for those of us who are doing CME courses and reading journals and learning new stuff all the time. And now we have to study for another board exam! Well, to be honest, it is not that hard. Of course, I work in family practice and I do talk with physicians, read my journals and learn all the time. If you keep up on your knowledge, this exam is nothing to get worked up about. The problem is that not everyone keeps learning like they should so we do need some way to encourage PAs to maintain a certain level of knowledge in order to stay in practice. The ability to pass an exam of this type gives the NCCPA one more tool to maintain the professional standards of knowledge and skills. This brings up the next big controversial topic facing our profession…specialty certification.

I have a friend named Bob. He has been practicing medicine since graduating from his PA program in 1979. He works at Childrens Hospital

Los Angeles where he supervises other PAs in the hematology/oncology department. He works in pediatric hematology and further specializes in coagulation (blood clotting and bleeding disorders). He sees patients and does research in addition to having full faculty privileges and teaching at the USC PA program. He is also a guest lecturer for other PA and medical students. He gets asked to speak internationally at all these big scientific conventions where physicians are sharing the latest research and discoveries in the pediatric coagulation world. He is amazing. I try to avoid having a conversation about medicine with Bob because he is so smart and it is somewhat intimidating for me!

All right, I am getting to the controversy now. Say Bob's 6 year cycle is ending and he needs to recertify. The CME logging is no problem – he goes to conferences and reads his journals. Heck, Bob *teaches* CME. If he sits down to take the recertification exam, he faces lots of questions about type 2 diabetes, depression, heart disease and kids' immunization schedules. No one would question that Bob is a great PA and should be able to maintain certification. But, he is the first to admit that he does not have time or interest in keeping up on primary care issues – he counts on those of us in primary care to do that. So, it seems even more pointless and silly to have him sit down and read about the diagnosis and management of Alzheimer's disease just so he can pass a test. Obviously, this is not Bob's issue; he just said I could use him as an example. But, as PAs like Bob are getting more specialized and being utilized in very unique and focused roles, the idea of recertifying everyone in primary care seems outdated.

The NCCPA reacted to this concern by developing a Pathway II exam. Please don't focus too much on this, since it is being phased out in 2010. I just bring it up so you can understand the history. In an effort to address the concerns of the specialized PA, this "take home" exam was developed. It allowed Bob to have a packet of questions that he could then research and answer on his own time which provided some education to him about what is going on in primary care, but also gave him a little less stress in that he didn't need to study for an exam and stress about not passing. It was a good solution for some, but there were many complaints that it took too much time and that there was no control over who was actually answering the questions. The exam was difficult and some PAs found that more than one answer seemed correct even when verifying with multiple resources. So, what's next? We have been struggling for years with the idea of having a specialty exam. Thus far, the NCCPA has developed a weighted test so that you can choose one of three tests – adult medicine, primary care, and surgery. There is still a test of knowledge of primary care in all of the exams, but there are more questions about surgery in the surgery exam and more questions about adult medicine in the adult medicine exam. That still doesn't help poor Bob very much.

Why don't we just start getting a specialty certification like the physicians do? If you were a physician who did your residency in urology and you passed your board certification in that field, then your recertification exam is in urology, not in primary care. Ah, but remember what I said one of the most beautiful things about the PA profession was? OK, I will remind you. It is that we can change our specialty throughout our career. If the NCCPA starts offering multiple exams or starts supporting a specialty board concept, will that preclude me from working in a specialty *unless* I pass the specialty exam? Does that limit the flexibility of my license? Will I have an option or will employers start requiring specialty certification? Maybe insurance companies won't allow you to bill for services in a specialty unless you become specialty certified. How many specialty certifications should we have? There are no answers to these questions because our profession is still trying to figure out how to make all of this work. However, the trend seems to be *toward* offering PAs who work in a specialty the option of becoming certified in that specialty.

The NCCPA released a Public Statement Regarding NCCPA's Commitment to Offer a Voluntary Credential for PAs Practicing in Specialties[9]

> *After several years of thoughtful consideration of how to best serve the public interest and discussions with numerous PA and physician specialty organizations and others, at a February 8, 2009 meeting, NCCPA's Board of Directors reaffirmed its commitment to offering a mechanism for the achievement of a voluntary PA specialty credential.*

---

9   http://www.nccpa.net/News_A_SpecialtyCredential.aspx

> *An NCCPA workgroup is developing the model for a specialty credential program, which the organization will launch no later than 2011. As the model develops, NCCPA will continue to work with AAPA and physician and PA specialty organizations in the discussions.*
>
> *NCCPA is committed to engaging others in dialogue about the specific elements of the specialty credential program and to considering their input. Written comments can be submitted to NCCPA by email and should be directed to comments@nccpa.net.*

It is important to know that there are PAs who sit on the NCCPA Board of Directors and that the AAPA has input to the NCCPA. But, they are separate organizations and they do not always agree about the right direction for the profession.

Let's go back and answer the earlier question of whether you have to maintain your certification. It is very important that if you decide NOT to maintain your certification that you do so only after much deliberation. First, look into the state laws. Some states require that you maintain NCCPA Certification in order to renew your PA license and continue to practice. Some employers, regardless of state law, will require that you maintain certification. If you chose not to meet the requirements of certification, you can still practice in some states, but you cannot use the PA-C title. You are, in that case, officially a PA, not a PA-C. If you ever want to go back to regain certification after losing it, you will need to start again by sitting for the <u>initial</u> certifying exam or by logging 300 hours of CME in the past 6 years and sitting for the recertification exam.

See? You even got through the dry, boring and kinda scary stuff! Take it upon yourself to stay involved in your profession. Reach out to the state regulatory board for information regularly and maintain your membership in your state PA academy (and actually read the stuff you get from them!) and you will know what you need to know to keep clean. Laws change and regulations get updated. Being a licensed professional means you are responsible for staying current and now you have the tools to do just that.

Your Physician Assistant Association

Most professions have a professional organization that you can join. Some are very active, doing a lot of good things for the profession; some are more social and some seem to have a bunch of meetings but not accomplish much! Why would you need to join these types of organizations? More importantly, why would I devote an entire chapter to explain the importance? What do they do besides take your dues? As a PA, we have so much money going out for license, certification, continuing education, books and journals do we really need to spend another few hundred dollars joining an organization? The answer is a resounding "Yes." These are the things that are expected of a professional and, really, these are minimal expenses for someone who is making a professional salary. So, keep it in perspective.

Let's start with before you get into school. Say you are looking into the profession and you haven't gotten the answer to that one last question that this book didn't answer. Where will you find the answer? Likely, you will find it either at the AAPA or your state chapter of the AAPA. It is not essential to join at that point. They will likely have the information on their website or gladly help you over the phone. But, you might look into membership even before applying to school. One benefit is the newsletters. You can see what the hot issues are for the profession. When you sit for an interview and you reference a local or national issue for the profession, the interviewer will probably be impressed that you were motivated to acquire that knowledge. You might even want to go to a conference. Most states and the AAPA put on at least an annual education conference. You may not understand the lectures completely, but it will expose you to the type of lifelong learning that we do as PAs. You will also meet a PA or two that wouldn't mind telling you about her job and what she likes or dislikes about it. If you are very lucky, you might meet a faculty member at the program to which you want to apply. Now you can discuss and inquire whether their program fits with your goals.

Ok, so now you are a student. This is the time to really take advantage!! Student memberships are cheap! We know it is tough to be a student and the expenses can be overwhelming and you probably aren't bringing in much of an income while you're in school. But, PAs also know how important it is to have student members in their organizations. We want students to get involved in their profession while they are young. You bring a fresh view and a lot of energy to an organization! We love that. You still get most of the benefits of membership while you are a student including newsletters and maybe even access to job postings. The AAPA has scholarships that you may be eligible for if you are a student and the state in which you live or go to school may have a chapter that offers scholarships for members. Students also can usually attend conferences pretty cheap, so look into that as well. Again, depending on how long you have been in the program, lectures may sound a bit intense and over your head, but more than likely you will be surprised at how much you understand. Again, the next big benefit of conferences is that you are surrounded by PAs. You could meet a PA that could be your next preceptor or a future connection for a job!

It is never too early to look into being a leader in your profession. The AAPA has numerous opportunities to get involved as a student. Depending on the program you attend, you may or may not hear about these opportunities unless you are really looking or you hear from another PA or PA student. Most PA programs have some sort of student government within the class – at least a class president. A student in your class should be in contact with the AAPA and the state organization to see how best to act as a liaison between the students and that organization. That person should be getting information to you as well. The first exposure you may have to opportunities within the AAPA is at the AAPA annual conference. This conference moves around yearly. The current strategy is to move it from the west coast, central, then east coast. This may change since we are "outgrowing" some of the popular destinations and we will be limited at some point to certain larger venues. It traditionally falls over the Memorial Day weekend in honor of the military "fathers" of our profession.

At the conference, the Student Academy holds the Assembly of Representatives (AOR). Now, when I was a first year student in 1994, I attended this sort of informal gathering of students down in San Antonio, TX, and we talked about issues affecting specific programs or students in general. We followed *Sturgis Rules of Order* and presented resolutions, but you could tell it was pretty low key. Today it is a different story. This is a very professionally run meeting. You shouldn't be intimidated if you have never been to an association meeting, but you will also need to make sure you have a mentor there to show you how to present a resolution or debate on a subject. It is so exciting for me now during the conference to see how much the students accomplish. They hold elections, debate issues and set up committees for the upcoming year. Plan to attend the AAPA meeting if possible and consider at least watching some of the AOR meeting early in the conference. Your PA program will have a seat at the AOR so you should ask how your program identifies a student to attend. But, even if you are not the delegate from your program, you can still watch the proceedings from a public viewing area.

The Student Board of Directors (SBOD) of the AAPA[1] contains nine student positions. Each year, students vote for their new SBOD during the Assembly of Representatives (AOR) held at AAPA's annual conference. Seven positions are elected annually: president, vice president, chief delegate, director of diversity, director of internal affairs, director of external affairs junior, and the special projects coordinator. The president from the previous year returns as the immediate past president and the director of external affairs junior becomes the director of external affairs senior for the upcoming year. In addition to the nine elected positions, there are eight other leadership positions. These positions are the following: the five regional chairs, Physician Assistants Education Association (PAEA) student member at large, Physician Assistant Foundation (PAF) marketing and communications committee student representative, and the Physician Assistant Foundation resource development committee student representative. Student leadership is assisted by an AAPA graduate advisor, PAEA graduate advisor, and the AAPA staff advisors. Holding

---

1   http://www.saaapa.aapa.org

a SBOD position while you are a student is a tremendous experience. I was lucky enough to officially spend three years on the student board as secretary, president, and then immediate past president. I still cherish the education, experiences and relationships I built during those years. It involves travel to AAPA headquarters in Alexandria, VA as well as other locations which is tough to fit into an already busy school schedule. It also requires the support of your PA program, since the travel may take you away from school commitments. I would highly recommend making it a priority. See what the positions are like at the conference and think about getting involved early.

The AAPA also holds a House of Delegates (HOD) meeting during the AAPA Annual conference and this is where AAPA Policy is created, position papers are adopted and elections for the HOD leadership are held. At this meeting, each constituent organization within the AAPA is seated including a large student contingency. Although there is not nearly enough student seats to have every program represented, every program is encouraged to identify a student to participate in the HOD. There is a chief student delegate who manages to rotate students in and out of the designated student seats for voting purposes, while the remainder of the student delegation listens to the proceedings from the public audience area. This, too, is a great experience as a student. You can learn a lot about the real issues facing the profession and the different arguments for and against the proposed positions.

At the state organization, you can also get involved as a student if you prefer to make your impact at a more local level. You can access information about your state constituent chapter through the AAPA website. Consider running for the student representative on the Board of Directors (BOD). If your state doesn't have a student on the BOD currently, inquire about it. Sometimes there is a position but previously no interest, so it wasn't filled. You might want to call one of the current board members to see what it would be like to be on the board, or talk with the student currently in that position. You can attend a BOD meeting and they should be happy to have you. We rarely get guests at the meetings and most boards would love a student to attend at least a portion. If you call ahead you can find out the best time to attend and get an idea of what the meetings are like. Your program should also have some relationship with your state organization so students can become members and find out about events for students in that state. Inquire about state conferences. There may be a specific student track or student event you should know about. If you are planning on working in a state other than the one in which your program is located, you may consider instead joining the association of the state that you are moving back to. This will help keep you more informed about the issues you will be facing upon graduation.

Now that you have graduated, what do you need your professional organization for? Aren't the people involved pretty much just spending dues dollars to get together and attend meetings? What do we really need that for? To me, this is so important I devoted a whole chapter to it! And, it should be that important to you as well. Remember how young we are? You are right, our profession is only as old this author and that is YOUNG. We have so much more to do to get a strong hold on our future. There are states with only hundreds of PAs practicing. We need to be there for each other and support the growth of our profession. Everyone has a different limit to what they can offer. You may think I am crazy to want to spend my days off travelling to the state capitol with our lobbyist talking about PAs. Maybe *want* is a strong word. But, I found for me, it is something I *can* do and *should* do because I want PAs to be known, accepted and have no legal barriers to be able to practice the way we have been educated to practice. I would feel guilty just sitting here in this great career and not giving something back to make it even better! You may not have a lot of time. But, I know for a fact that if you have a job as a physician assistant anywhere in this country, you have enough money to at least pay dues to your state chapter, your specialty organization (if available) and to the AAPA. So, where does that money go and what do they do for you anyway?

I asked Bill Leinweber, EVP/CEO of the AAPA to answer the question – "Why should I become a member of the AAPA?" for you.

> *When you join the AAPA, you become part of the only national association dedicated to enhancing the practice environment for all physician assistants. Membership provides you with benefits*

and services designed to take your professional development to the next level. Connect with your peers by accessing networking and volunteer opportunities, expand your base of learning while fulfilling your CME requirements with our extensive library of free and low-cost CME, and stay up-to-date on the latest medical breakthroughs and profession advances with the Journal of the American Academy of Physician Assistants and AAPA News.

The American Academy of Physician Assistants, established in 1968, represents physician assistants in every practice setting and specialty. AAPA has more than 42,000 members representing every state and territory. The AAPA is governed by the House of Delegates (HOD), policy-making body, and Board of Directors, which carries out the policies of the house.

The Academy has a federated structure of chartered constituent chapters in the 50 states, the District of Columbia, the U.S. territories, the Air Force, Navy, Army Public Health Service, and Department of Veteran Affairs. In addition, AAPA officially recognizes PA specialty organizations, caucuses, congresses, and special interest groups.

Advocacy

Do you think that when physicians and nurses get together with legislators to make a new law, say about access to affordable health care services, that anyone thinks about PAs? Unfortunately, much of the time PAs are not included. We tend to be an afterthought, or not even considered at all. So every year thousands of bills are introduced in both the Congress and in each individual state. A good percentage of these bills are somehow related to health care. What if all this legislation got passed – good or bad – and none of it mentioned PAs? That would be disastrous for our profession! It takes a lot of staff time and often hired contracted legislative advocates to track legislation to make sure that PAs are included where appropriate. Not a lot of professions need to advocate for itself this way. Sure, physician associations need to make sure that someone isn't going to pass something that would cost too much money or time or put undue pressure on their office. That is a huge task already. But, rarely would a health bill be introduced without someone including the physician organization's opinion and without considering what affect it would have on a physician's office. Since we tend to be the afterthought, we have to work even harder to ensure that PAs are considered and added in to appropriate bills. Oftentimes this is not a monumental task – we ask the author to include us, prepare language, and then watch the bill. But, we need to do this with many health care bills on a national level and on the state level. And, we need people who know the right people to get this task done and to help fix it when it starts going wrong.

Some states still have restrictive language in their laws and regulations and it is very frustrating to PAs practicing in that state. If a state PA organization is going to introduce a bill to fix a problem in that state, they need the resources to do that. The AAPA can help by providing manpower and data through its absolutely amazing State Government Affairs staff, but the state needs to lead the way and provide the bulk of the funding and time. Language needs to be reviewed by legal counsel, bills need to be introduced by legislative advocates and PAs need to travel to the capitol to explain to legislators the need for the bill and to attend hearings. All of this takes time and money which comes largely from dues dollars.

Reimbursement

You read in chapter three that many specialty organizations are struggling with reimbursement for the procedures they do. Physicians are concerned about this as well. There are issues with billing accurately and appropriately, but there are also times the payer needs to be educated about physician assistants. There are still insurance companies that do not recognize our profession or are unclear as to why we are billing for physician services if we are not physicians. Again, this takes an extraordinary amount of staff time especially for the AAPA to address these concerns on a national level. AAPA staff knows reimbursement and understands the issues PAs are facing in attempting to bill properly and get paid for services. They are in contact with PA offices, insurance companies and other payers to make sure they understand the billing process and reimbursement. If you have a special circumstance where billing is a particular issue, the AAPA can help you individually at the office level.

Conferences and Continuing Education

So, if I have to get 100 hours of continuing education every 2 years, I can pretty much get it from anywhere these days, right? Yes, that is right. You can go on-line, read journals and even attend physician conferences. They all meet the requirement as long as they are accredited. So what does a PA conference have that other resources don't? You got it – PAs!! Going to the AAPA conference is the only place every year that you can see PAs who taught you, PAs you went to school with, PAs you have been in leadership with, and PAs that you have only heard about but have always wanted to meet. Lectures are given by PAs, as well as physicians, along with a few other healthcare providers and they vary in specialty. It is the conference FOR PAs put on BY PAs and it is uniquely special because the attendees are PAs. Now as special as the AAPA conference is, the state conferences and specialty conference can be even more focused and relevant for you. Again, it is more about the people than anything else. Since these conferences are smaller, you have even more time to spend with your old classmates and PAs you have learned from, worked with, or mentored.

Marketing and Public Relations

So, just how has it happened that PAs are becoming more accepted? Many say it is because we are all out there practicing good medicine and making patients aware of who we are and the word is finally spreading. That is probably a good part of it. But, the other part is our PA associations. The AAPA and your state and specialty organizations are working hard to make sure good stories about PAs are published in the paper, PAs are recognized in news events, and that word gets out to our physician employers and the general public about our profession. They also make sure that PAs are included in health care policies and planning. They are helping PAs to apply for or step into high profile positions that lead to our recognition. They are supporting programs and other associations that include physician assistants. This is how the public and our employers are becoming more familiar and starting to really understand what it is we do.

Support the PAC

Political Action Committee (PAC) is a popular term for a political committee formed by business, labor, or other special-interest groups to raise money and make contributions to the campaigns of political candidates they support[2]. These contributions are not tax deductible and are tracked carefully.

Contributions from the AAPA PAC[3] "support the primary and general election campaign efforts of candidates for the U.S. Congress who support and promote the principles of the PA profession and who advocate for policies that improve the health care environment for physician-PA teams and their patients. The AAPA PAC does not contribute to political parties, to presidential candidates, or to other political action committees. The AAPA PAC supports both Republican and Democratic candidates with a proven record of supporting and promoting AAPA's legislative priorities. Special consideration is given to candidates who have worked closely with PAs in the past, for example by sponsoring key legislation, and to candidates who hold positions on congressional committees that directly impact AAPA's legislative goals. The AAPA PAC may only make contributions to candidates seeking federal elective office; it cannot support state or local candidates."

Similarly, your state and/or specialty organization may have PACs that you can contribute to. It is a vital component to our success as a profession to be able to make campaign contributions to candidates who understand and support physician assistants. Because our numbers are small, it is even more important for every PA to plan to contribute to this valuable fund on an annual basis.

PA Foundation
Like many national organizations, the AAPA has a Foundation (PAF)[4] or philanthropic association that is giving back to PAs, PA students and the community. Watch your mail, email and the AAPA website to see what the Foundation is working on. The Foundation relies on contributions from PAs as well as from industry donors in order to continue the good work they do. The PAF has awarded hundreds of scholarships to PA students.

---

2   http://www.usa.gov

3   http://www.aapa.org/gandp/pac

4   http://www.aapa.org/paf/

They fund community outreach projects and participate in an annual campaign which identifies and donates to a local project near the area of the AAPA Conference. Make an annual donation to the PAF a priority.

I know you are thinking I have you working every day just to pay back to all this stuff. In reality, though, you may end up spending maybe 1-2% of your salary on an annual basis to further your profession. If you are lucky, your employer will pay for your membership fees and/or conference registration. They may even match your contribution to the PA Foundation. If not, then much of this is tax deductible. So, keep it in perspective and do your part in continuing to make this one of the best professions in America.

Get a Life!

Being a PA really must be the greatest profession there is at this time. I can't believe I was lucky enough to find the PA profession when I did and to get to a point where I can write a book about it to share the experience with others, and hopefully inspire a couple of readers! This career allows you to help others, work with amazing physicians and be involved in medicine, one of the most exciting and evolving fields.

This chapter is devoted to helping you remember to take care of yourself as well as you take care of others. If you are still in school, you may put this away and forget it for a while. After all, I spent a whole chapter telling you that you will eat, sleep and drink medicine for two years in PA school. So, keep this around and take it out again after you have been out for a year. And, remember that balance in your life is the real key to happiness.

When we are in school or working in the hospital with crazy hours and intense work, we all complain. You will too. We say how tired we are and how no one should work like this. But, there is also something very invigorating about it. There is something that makes you feel like you have accomplished even more if it is 2:00 in the morning when you do it. You can easily get caught up in the excitement of the emergency room and the challenge of an intense surgery. Being able to take on these challenges is fulfilling and somewhat addicting. There is certainly nothing wrong with having passion for the work you do, but it's important not to let your work become an addiction. Here are some suggestions to help keep your life in balance.

Get a Calendar
It probably isn't really a calendar, but a Palm®, a Blackberry® or an iPhone™. Your calendar at work is most likely an electronic medical record filled with patient's names every 15 minutes. You should have a separate, personal calendar with social and family engagements on it. Keep all of your appointments in one place and don't forget to put in the kids' schedule so

you don't forget to get them to practice on time. Include any meetings for work and school. Now, make sure you schedule your "me" time and write it down. One sure way to schedule time for yourself is to simply put it on your calendar. It may be a pedicure or a massage or going out with friends – whatever you want. But, if it isn't scheduled, you are much less likely to get it done! My mom has a masseuse named Debbie. She sees her on the first Tuesday of every month without fail. I used to laugh at her and tell her she could skip it if something else comes up, but she never does because she has made it a priority to take care of herself. She has the time blocked out on her schedule and nothing ever conflicts with it.

Get a Doctor (perhaps one with a PA!?)

You will be amazed at the number of medical professionals who do not take care of themselves physically. We need to remember that we are humans as well. We are not less vulnerable to disease than someone not in medicine. We don't need our preventative care and cancer screenings any less that our friends and patients who work in other industries. And, really, you have no excuse. You have access to care, for certain. So, stay up-to-date on your pap smears and mammograms. Get your prostate checked and schedule your colonoscopy. You sound a lot less like a hypocrite when you are encouraging your patients to do a screening test if you are up-to-date. If a patient asks, you can proudly say that you did that already. I talk about this stuff with my patients and I tell them that I go through it, too. Unfortunately, I was asked once by a patient if I thought the prep was terrible for my colonoscopy since she had just done one. This is a test that is currently indicated for screening starting at age 50 and since I was only 38 at the time, it ruined my whole day!

You might get your services at your own office or that of a friend, or you might just find a family doctor who doesn't know you professionally. You need to make that call and get in for your preventative stuff. It is also important to have a real relationship with your health care provider. Often physicians and other health care professionals are tempted to treat themselves. There are samples of many drugs in the cupboard or you could probably convince someone you know to write you a prescription. You should have more respect for your body than that. If you are ill or have symptoms, even if you "know" what is wrong, it is important to just give in and be a patient and let someone else care for you. Who knows, you might learn something along the way!

Take good care of your body and don't forget to take good care of your mental health and memory. It is vital to long life. John "Coach" Wooden, the legendary former UCLA basketball coach and educator, is a prime example of perfect aging. Just before his 98th birthday, he was interviewed by Alan Castel[1], Assistant Professor of Psychology at the University of California, Los Angeles. "When asked about the keys to successful aging, Coach was quick to respond: stay busy, stay active, enjoy every day like it is your masterpiece, have some variety and try to learn something new every day," Castel said. "One of Coach's famous quotes, 'When I am through learning, then I am through,' illustrates his lifelong commitment to learning."

Get a Hobby

Medicine is so consuming, you need a distraction. It takes a lot to keep up in your field. You have to read journals and research and go to classes. You will need something that you like to do that does not involve talking with patients or reading about the new guidelines for optimal control of asthma. Get back to doing something you used to love or try something new. Do something with your family or friends *and* do something that is all yours.

My family's hobby is UCLA. You might have thought that it was just a well-respected University with a fine athletic program, being the first in the country to reach 100 national championships. But, it is not just a school. It is our hobby. We have had season tickets to UCLA football since I graduated in 1990. Each game takes the entire Saturday. We meet early in the morning and spend the day catching up with our friends. We play softball or football outside the Rose Bowl and BBQ our favorite dish. We know the ushers and the alumni cheerleaders and look forward to seeing them. We also go to basketball games, gymnastics meets and softball games on campus. We have a long history at the school and with the friends we meet up with there. And for the entire day we don't do any work!

---

1   http://www.psychologicalscience.org/observer/getArticle.cfm?id=2466

Our relatively new hobby is softball, which is my daughter's passion and my husband's obsession. I watch and take pictures and sometimes they let me be "dugout mom." But, we are all there as a family, enjoying watching my daughter excel and experience her first true passion. That has become an all day affair as well since we watch other games and cheer on our friends.

Believe it or not, when I have time alone I like to sew. My mom is an amazing seamstress – made my prom dresses and my sister's wedding gown. I'll never be that good, but I try. When my kid was a baby it was fun to make her Halloween costumes and little dresses. It gave me a sense of accomplishment – they are small projects mostly, and you can set a goal, complete it and show off your work. It is fun. Now she doesn't let me make anything for her because I can't make anything cool enough, but I find other little projects and get them done!

Get Exercise

Set a good example for your patients and help yourself feel better while you're at it. I cannot imagine my life if I didn't run. I get cranky if I take a week off now. I have always been active, but felt it was more of a chore. I would go to the gym and take classes, but always with the intension of taking off some weight, like most women I guess. I never really *liked* it. OK, maybe I did like those step aerobic classes when that was the fad, but it was hard to make it to the classes on their schedule, so I got burned out.

After I became a PA, a medical assistant I was working with named Jen encouraged me to run a 5K. "I can't run" I would tell her. She said we all can run, which was true, really. I guess what I meant was that I couldn't run *fast*. She said that didn't matter, it just mattered that I ran. So, let me understand - I don't have to try to *win* the race, I could just get out there and finish it? Oh, now I get it! Who knew that most runners run to run and not to win? Sadly, Jen died way too young of a terrible infection only a few months after that conversation, and I still thank her for opening my eyes to my current obsession. In fact, since she encouraged me to run my first 5K at the Turkey Trot on Thanksgiving morning in Dana Point, I still run that race for her every year. Over 10 years later, I have completed 11 marathons and my time hasn't improved much at all since my first… and it probably never will. I just love doing it – I love planning out my schedule for the next marathon and adjusting it along the way. I love spending so much time with my running partner and planning our get-a-ways for the next race. I always emphasize to patients and I will do the same for you - exercise needs to be something you like to do. Don't torture yourself! Play volleyball or basketball, lift weights, get a Wii Fit™, or do Taekwondo. It doesn't matter what you do, but if you aren't enjoying it, you probably won't keep doing it. There are enough other have-to's in life, so enjoy the things you have a choice about.

Saralyn and I run 2-3 days during the week and then do a "long" run on the weekends. I put long in quotes because it all depends on where we are in our training schedule. Sometimes long is 5 miles and sometimes it is 20. Not much throws us off our schedule unless we have a true illness or injury. Then we recover and get back on schedule. We run solo when we are on vacation. Sometimes we run with other people, but usually it is just the two of us. Psychologically we both feel better when we are running. I know I couldn't afford therapy 3 days a week and a counselor wouldn't be nearly as good as Saralyn anyway. When we run, we share our deepest secrets and our biggest fears. We talk about our day ahead and what type of challenges we are facing. We congratulate each other on our accomplishments and support each other when we are down. Saralyn knows more about my daily life than even my husband, because he and I don't always get an hour for each other by the end of the day!

Oh, and don't tell me you don't have time, because I have the perfect comeback and I use it. When patients tell me there is "never any time" to exercise, I ask them what they were doing at 5:30 that morning while I was running. Most of them don't really know what to say and at least it makes them think about their priorities. I tell them that I am one of the busiest people I know – I've got work, a kid, a husband, housecleaning, volunteer PA work, social engagements, writing a book – I still find time to exercise because it is important. It is important because it makes me feel better, I stay healthier, and I am setting a good example for my child and for my patients. I have actually encouraged a few friends and patients to run a marathon – my way of paying it forward for Jen.

Get Away

The joy of vacation! Wouldn't it be great to get away from it all and just relax? Maybe you are doing that right now. You need to schedule your vacation and take it. Life is short. You need to get out and enjoy the world around you before it is too late. Right after I got married, I started PA school and my husband, Brian, was working full-time and going to school at night to get his MBA. Good thing our relationship was solid going into *that* marriage! I think about 5 years went by when we realized we hadn't taken a vacation since our honeymoon. Yeah, we had taken a couple weekends away to Lake Tahoe or something, but not a real vacation. We couldn't. We were in school and then we had new jobs and no vacation time. Then one weekend we went on a timeshare tour and purchased one! That may not be the answer for you, but it works for us. We now take at least 2 full week-long vacations every year without fail. We really cannot *forget* to schedule it because you need to get in your request so early. It forces us to sit down, pick a time and place and then we schedule it right then. We have travelled to Europe and Mexico and all over the USA to places we wouldn't normally have ventured to.

Your perfect vacation may be a trip to the beach or going camping. It doesn't need to be exotic or expensive. Do a romantic get away for two, or travel with another family. Take a tour to someplace you have always dreamed of going. Consider a cruise or an all-inclusive resort so you don't have to do the planning. Or, just pack a bag and get in the car and drive. Be safe and cautious and have fun!

Get a Perspective

It doesn't take long to find a patient that really opens your eyes, someone who you really relate to, to make you realize what you have. Just like any job, your days as a PA can get very routine. There are days in the middle of the winter that I can't wait to see somebody other than a person with sinusitis or bronchitis. It usually is just about then that you see someone that changes your attitude. There is the single mom that is managing her autistic child, the deaf child that has learned to sign with his sister, the breast cancer survivor. Please, stop to listen to these patients. Let them teach you to pay attention and to have the **patience** to help others. Don't take anything for granted. Ask them how they are managing to get through the day. Find out what is holding them back and what has helped them. By listening to the *person* behind the patient you will help yourself and ultimately help your other patients. As crazy as life can get and as self-consumed as our world has become, we still can learn so much from each other if we just take a minute to see the talents and gifts in the people with whom we interact.

Don't forget to reward good behavior. Give a child a sticker if he sat patiently waiting for Dad to get his blood pressure rechecked. Make note and congratulate a diabetic patient that lost 10 pounds since his last visit. Ask about whether your patient still is refraining from smoking and tell her you are proud she stopped.

Get Help

This is a stressful career. Although you are well-trained and competent, there will be times when you doubt yourself and your abilities. After all, you are making clinical decisions that could adversely affect another human being. You may feel guilty after a patient passes away even if you did everything you could have for her. You may start feeling anxious about seeing certain types of patients if you had a case with a bad outcome. You might get depressed working in a particularly emotional specialty where outcomes are grim. Some of these feelings are very normal and expected, but sometimes they start affecting your work. Do not be afraid to get help. That is what you would advise a patient to do! Don't think you know so much about medicine that you cannot be helped by going to therapy after a traumatic incident or after a loss. Watch for signs of inability to cope and address them early.

Medical professionals historically have a slighter higher than average rate of dependence on or overuse of drugs and alcohol. We are at higher risk due to access to controlled substances and ability to self-treat. In addition, we could face the same risks as the general public including family history of substance abuse and chronic stress. Familiarize yourself with the laws in your state regarding impaired healthcare workers; recognize the signs of drug use and alcohol overuse in yourself and your colleagues. If you have a problem and need help, contact your state licensing board or state PA association for more information. Don't ignore the problem and put your medical license, your career or your patients at risk.

Get Your Priorities Straight

author unknown

"I sat down one day and did a little arithmetic. The average person lives about seventy-five years. I know, some live more and some live less, but on average, folks live about seventy-five years.

Now then, I multiplied 75 times 52 and I came up with 3900, which is the number of Saturdays that the average person has in their entire lifetime. It took me until I was 55 years old to think about all this in any detail, and by that time I had lived through over 2800 Saturdays. I got to thinking that if I lived to be 75, I only had about a thousand of them left to enjoy. So I went to a toy store and bought every single marble they had. I ended up having to visit three toy stores to round up 1000 marbles. I took them home and put them inside of a large, clear plastic container right here in my workshop next to the radio. Every Saturday since then, I have taken one marble out and thrown it away.

I found that by watching the marbles diminish, I focused more on the really important things in life. There is nothing like watching your time here on this earth run out to help get your priorities straight.

Now let me tell you one last thing before I sign-off with you and take my lovely wife out for breakfast. This morning, I took the very last marble out of the container. I figure if I make it until next Saturday, then I have been given a little extra time. And the one thing we can all use is a little more time."

Get Going

I have filled your brain with everything I know about this amazing profession. Now, it is up to you to decide what to do. You may have just a little bit to accomplish to get your application perfect, or you may have a couple of years of classes and volunteer work to do. Either way, if you like what you read and you want to join this group of outstanding professionals, start working toward that goal! Find the program that is perfect for you, along with a couple alternative choices or close seconds. See what is required and get it done. The sooner you start moving toward your goal, the sooner you will attain it. Find a mentor, join a PA organization, and get involved. Before you know it, you will be a contributor to my next edition!

Specialty Organizations
recognized by the
American Academy of Physician Assistants

American Academy of Nephrology PAs
www.aanpa.org

American Academy of PAs in Occupational Medicine
www.aapaoccmed.org

American Academy PAs in Allergy Asthma and Immunology
www.aapa-aai.com

American Association of Surgical PAs
www.aaspa.com

American Society of Endocrine Physician Assistants
www.endocrine-pa.com

Association of Family Practice PAs
www.afppa.org

Association of Neurosurgical Physician Assistants
www.anspa.org

Association of PAs in Cardiology
http://cardiologypa.org

Association of PAs in Cardiovascular Surgery
www.apacvs.org

Association of PAs in Obstetrics & Gynecology
www.paobgyn.org

Association of PAs in Oncology
http://apao.cc

Association of Physician Assistants in Anesthesia
www.paanesthesiaworld.us

Association of Plastic Surgery PAs
www.apspa.net/new

Gastroenterology Physician Assistants
www.gipas.org

PAs in Orthopedic Surgery
www.paos.org

Physician Assistants in Psychiatry
www.psychpa.com

Society for PAs in Pediatrics
www.spaponline.org

Society of Dermatology PAs
www.dermpa.org

Society of Emergency Medicine PAs
www.sempa.org

Society of PAs Caring for the Elderly
www.geri-pa.org

Society of PAs in Addiction Medicine
www.spaam.net

Society of PAs in Otorhinolaryngology/Head & Neck Surgery
www.entpa.org

Society of PAs in Rheumatology
www.rheumpas.org

Urological Association of PAs
www.uapanet.org

You can also find contact information and website links for Special Interest Groups in some additional medical specialties and in more specific groups within a specialty. This information is available through the AAPA at https://members.aapa.org/extra/constituents/sig-menu.cfm.

State PA Regulatory Boards

ALABAMA
www.albme.org
(334) 242-4116

ALASKA
www.dced.state.ak.us/occ/pmed
(907) 269-8163

ARIZONA
www.azpa.gov
(480) 551-2700

ARKANSAS
www.armedicalboard.org
(501) 296-1802

CALIFORNIA
www.pac.ca.gov
(916) 561-8780

COLORADO
www.dora.state.co.us/medical
(303) 894-7690

CONNECTICUT
www.ct.gov/dph
(860) 509-7603

DELAWARE
www.dpr.delaware.gov/boards
/medicalpractice
(302) 744-4500

DISTRICT OF COLUMBIA
http://hpla.doh.dc.gov/hpla/cwp
/view,A,1195,Q,488575.asp
(877) 672-2174

FLORIDA
www.doh.state.fl.us/mqa/PhysAsst/
(850) 488-0595

GEORGIA
http://medicalboard.georgia.gov/02/csbme
/home/0,2458,26729866,00.html
(404) 656-3913

GUAM
http://dphss.guam.gov/about/licensing.htm
(011) (671)735-7406

HAWAII	http://hawaii.gov/dcca/areas/pvl/boards/medical (808) 586-3000
IDAHO	www.bom.state.id.us (208) 327-7000
ILLINOIS	www.idfpr.com/dpr/WHO/adjmed.asp (217) 785-0800
INDIANA	www.in.gov/pla/pa.htm (317) 234-2060
IOWA	www.idph.state.ia.us/licensure/board_home.asp?board=pa (515) 281-4401
KANSAS	www.ksbha.org (785) 296-7413
KENTUCKY	http://kbml.ky.gov/ah/pa.htm (502) 429-7150
LOUISIANA	www.lsbme.louisiana.gov (504) 599-0503
MAINE	www.docboard.org/me/me_home.htm (207) 287-3601
MARYLAND	www.mbp.state.md.us/pages/phys_assi.html (800) 492-6836
MASSACHUSETTS	www.mass.gov/dpl/boards/ap/index.htm (800) 414-0168
MICHIGAN	www.michigan.gov/mdch/0,1607,7-132-27417_27529_27550---,00.html (517) 335-0918

MINNESOTA	www.state.mn.us/portal/mn/jsp/home.do?agency=BMP (612) 617-2130
MISSISSIPPI	www.msbml.state.ms.us (601) 987-3079
MISSOURI	http://pr.mo.gov/physicianassistants.asp (866) 289-5753
MONTANA	http://mt.gov/dli/bsd/license/bsd_boards/med_board/licenses/med/lic_pac.asp (406) 841-2364
NEBRASKA	www.dhhs.ne.gov/crl/medical/medsur/pa/pa.htm (402) 471-2118
NEVADA	http://medboard.nv.gov (888) 890-8210 or (775) 688-2559
NEW HAMPSHIRE	www.nh.gov/medicine/assistants (603) 271-1203
NEW JERSEY	www.state.nj.us/lps/ca/medical/pa.htm (973) 504-6580
NEW MEXICO	www.nmmb.state.nm.us (505) 476-7220 or (800) 945-5845
NEW YORK	www.op.nysed.gov/rpa.htm (518) 474-3817 ext. 560
NORTH CAROLINA	www.ncmedboard.org (919) 326-1100 or (800) 253-9653
NORTH DAKOTA	www.ndbomex.com (701) 328-6500
OHIO	www.med.ohio.gov/pa_whats_new.htm (614) 466-3934

OKLAHOMA	www.osbmls.state.ok.us (405) 848-6841
OREGON	www.oregon.gov/OMB/UmbrellaPA.shtml (971) 673-2700 or (877) 254-6263
PENNSYLVANIA	www.dos.state.pa.us/bpoa/medbd /mainpage.htm (717) 783-1400
RHODE ISLAND	www.health.ri.gov/hsr/professions/phys _assist.php (401) 222-3855 or (800) 942-7434
SOUTH CAROLINA	www.llr.state.sc.us/POL/Medical (803) 896-4500
SOUTH DAKOTA	http://doh.sd.gov/boards/medicine (605) 367-7781
TENNESSEE	http://health.state.tn.us/Boards/PA /index.htm (615) 532-3202 or (800) 778-4123
TEXAS	www.tmb.state.tx.us/professionals /physicianassist/physicianassist.php (512) 305-7030
UTAH	www.dopl.utah.gov/licensing/physician _assistant.html (801) 530-6628 or (866) 275-3675
VERMONT	http://healthvermont.gov/hc/med_board /bmp.aspx (802) 863-7200 or (800) 464-4343
VIRGIN ISLANDS	www.fsmb.org/fcvs_paapp.html (888) 275-3287
VIRGINIA	www.dhp.state.va.us/medicine/default.htm (804) 367-4600

WASHINGTON
www.doh.wa.gov/hsqa/Professions
/Medical/default.htm
(360) 236-2750

WEST VIRGINIA
www.wvdhhr.org/wvbom/
(304) 558-2921

WISCONSIN
http://drl.wi.gov/boards/pac/index.htm
(608) 266-2112

WYOMING
http://wyomedboard.state.wy.us/
(307) 778-7053 or (800) 438-5784

Competencies for the Physician Assistant Profession
(Reprinted with permission from the publisher)

Preamble

In 2003, the National Commission on Certification of Physician Assistants (NCCPA) initiated an effort to define PA competencies in response to similar efforts being conducted within other health care professions and growing demand for accountability and assessment in clinical practice. The following year, representatives from three other national PA organizations, each bringing a unique perspective and valuable insights, joined NCCPA in that effort. Those organizations were the Accreditation Review Commission for Education of the Physician Assistant (ARC-PA), the body that accredits PA educational programs; the Association of Physician Assistant Programs (APAP), the membership association for PA educators and program directors; and the American Academy of Physician Assistants (AAPA), the only national membership association representing all PAs.

The resultant document, *Competencies for the Physician Assistant Profession*, is a foundation from which each of those four organizations, other physician assistant organizations and individual physician assistants themselves can chart a course for advancing the competencies of the PA profession.

Introduction

The purpose of this document is to communicate to the PA profession and the public a set of competencies that all physician assistants regardless of specialty or setting are expected to acquire and maintain throughout their careers. This document serves as a map for the individual PA, the physician-PA team and organizations that are committed to promoting the development and maintenance of these professional competencies among physician assistants.

The clinical role of PAs includes primary and specialty care in medical and surgical practice settings. Professional competencies1 for physician assistants include the effective and appropriate application of medical knowledge, interpersonal and communication skills, patient care, professionalism, practice-based learning and improvement, systems-based practice, as well as an unwavering commitment to continual learning, professional growth and the physician-PA team, for the benefit of patients and the larger community being served. These competencies are demonstrated within the scope of practice, whether medical or surgical, for each individual physician assistant as that scope is defined by the supervising physician and appropriate to the practice setting.

In 1999, the Accreditation Council for Graduation Medical Education (ACGME) endorsed a list of general competencies for medical residents. NCCPA's Eligibility Committee, with substantial input from representatives of AAPA, APAP and ARC-PA, has modified the ACGME's list for physician assistant practice, drawing from several other resources, including the work of Drs. Epstein and Hundert; research conducted by AAPA's EVP/CEO, Dr. Steve Crane; and NCCPA's own examination content blueprint.

PHYSICIAN ASSISTANT COMPETENCIES
Vers. 3.5 (3/22/05)

The PA profession defines the specific knowledge, skills, and attitudes required and provides educational experiences as needed in order for physician assistants to acquire and demonstrate these competencies.

MEDICAL KNOWLEDGE Medical knowledge includes an understanding of pathophysiology, patient presentation, differential diagnosis, patient management, surgical principles, health promotion and disease prevention. Physician assistants must demonstrate core knowledge about established and evolving biomedical and clinical sciences and the application of this knowledge to patient care in their area of practice. In addition, physician assistants are expected to demonstrate an investigatory and analytic thinking approach to clinical situations. Physician assistants are expected to:

- understand etiologies, risk factors, underlying pathologic process, and epidemiology for medical conditions

- identify signs and symptoms of medical conditions

- select and interpret appropriate diagnostic or lab studies

- manage general medical and surgical conditions to include understanding the indications, contraindications, side effects, interactions and adverse reactions of pharmacologic agents and other relevant treatment modalities

- identify the appropriate site of care for presenting conditions, including identifying emergent cases and those requiring referral or admission

- identify appropriate interventions for prevention of conditions

- identify the appropriate methods to detect conditions in an asymptomatic individual

- differentiate between the normal and the abnormal in anatomic, physiological, laboratory findings and other diagnostic data

- appropriately use history and physical findings and diagnostic studies to formulate a differential diagnosis

- provide appropriate care to patients with chronic conditions

INTERPERSONAL & COMMUNICATION SKILLS Interpersonal and communication skills encompass verbal, nonverbal and written exchange of information. Physician assistants must demonstrate interpersonal and communication skills that result in effective information exchange with patients, their patients' families, physicians, professional associates, and the health care system. Physician assistants are expected to:

- create and sustain a therapeutic and ethically sound relationship with patients

- use effective listening, nonverbal, explanatory, questioning, and writing skills to elicit and provide information

- appropriately adapt communication style and messages to the context of the individual patient interaction

- work effectively with physicians and other health care professionals as a member or leader of a health care team or other professional group

- apply an understanding of human behavior

- demonstrate emotional resilience and stability, adaptability, flexibility and tolerance of ambiguity and anxiety

- accurately and adequately document and record information regarding the care process for medical, legal, quality and financial purposes

PATIENT CARE Patient care includes age-appropriate assessment, evaluation and management. Physician assistants must demonstrate care that is effective, patient-centered, timely, efficient and equitable for the treatment of health problems and the promotion of wellness. Physician assistants are expected to:

- work effectively with physicians and other health care professionals to provide patient-centered care

- demonstrate caring and respectful behaviors when interacting with patients and their families

- gather essential and accurate information about their patients

- make informed decisions about diagnostic and therapeutic interventions based on patient information and preferences, up-to-date scientific evidence, and clinical judgment

- develop and carry out patient management plans

- counsel and educate patients and their families

- competently perform medical and surgical procedures considered essential in the area of practice

- provide health care services and education aimed at preventing health problems or maintaining health

PROFESSIONALISM Professionalism is the expression of positive values and ideals as care is delivered. Foremost, it involves prioritizing the interests of those being served above one's own. Physician assistants must know their professional and personal limitations. Professionalism also requires that PAs practice without impairment from substance abuse, cognitive deficiency or mental illness. Physician assistants must demonstrate a high level of responsibility, ethical practice, sensitivity to a diverse patient population and adherence to legal and regulatory requirements. Physician assistants are expected to demonstrate:

- understanding of legal and regulatory requirements, as well as the appropriate role of the physician assistant

- professional relationships with physician supervisors and other health care providers

- respect, compassion, and integrity

- responsiveness to the needs of patients and society

- accountability to patients, society, and the profession

- commitment to excellence and on-going professional development

- commitment to ethical principles pertaining to provision or withholding of clinical care, confidentiality of patient information, informed consent, and business practices

- sensitivity and responsiveness to patients' culture, age, gender, and disabilities

- self-reflection, critical curiosity and initiative

PRACTICE-BASED LEARNING AND IMPROVEMENT Practice-based learning and improvement includes the processes through which clinicians engage in critical analysis of their own practice experience, medical literature and other information resources for the purpose of self-improvement. Physician assistants must be able to assess, evaluate and improve their patient care practices. Physician assistants are expected to:

- analyze practice experience and perform practice-based improvement activities using a systematic methodology in concert with other members of the health care delivery team

- locate, appraise, and integrate evidence from scientific studies related to their patients' health problems

- obtain and apply information about their own population of patients and the larger population from which their patients are drawn

- apply knowledge of study designs and statistical methods to the appraisal of clinical studies and other information on diagnostic and therapeutic effectiveness

- apply information technology to manage information, access on-line medical information, and support their own education

- facilitate the learning of students and/or other health care professionals

- recognize and appropriately address gender, cultural, cognitive, emotional and other biases; gaps in medical knowledge; and physical limitations in themselves and others

SYSTEMS-BASED PRACTICE Systems-based practice encompasses the societal, organizational and economic environments in which health care is delivered. Physician assistants must demonstrate an awareness of and responsiveness to the larger system of health care to provide patient care that is of optimal value. PAs should work to improve the larger health care system of which their practices are a part. Physician assistants are expected to:

- use information technology to support patient care decisions and patient education

- effectively interact with different types of medical practice and delivery systems

- understand the funding sources and payment systems that provide coverage for patient care

- practice cost-effective health care and resource allocation that does not compromise quality of care

- advocate for quality patient care and assist patients in dealing with system complexities

- partner with supervising physicians, health care managers and other health care providers to assess, coordinate, and improve the delivery of health care and patient outcomes

- accept responsibility for promoting a safe environment for patient care and recognizing and correcting systems-based factors that negatively impact patient care

- apply medical information and clinical data systems to provide more effective, efficient patient care

- use the systems responsible for the appropriate payment of services

Breinigsville, PA USA
13 October 2010
247287BV00003B/3/P